Leicestershire and Rutland
WOODLANDS
Past and Present

Anthony Squires
Michael Jeeves

Kairos Press
Newtown Linford
Leicestershire
1994

Design and Layout by Robin Stevenson, Kairos Press.
Body text in Century Old Style 10.5 on 11.5
Imagesetting by CDS typeset, Leicester.
Reprographics by Midland Provincial Studios, Leicester.
Printed in Great Britain by Echo Press, Loughborough

British Library Cataloguing in Publication Data
A CIP catalogue record for this book is available from the British Library.

Cover Picture — Prior's Coppice in May.

Kairos Press
552 Bradgate Road
Newtown Linford
Leicestershire LE6 0HB

Contents

List of Figures

Overleaf: detail from 'Cornard Wood' by Thomas Gainsborough (1727 –1788)
A scene typical of woods held in common and not subject to firm manorial control. The signs of the decline of the woodland are evident: uncontrolled grazing by domestic stock; no regulation of access by the commoners to wood or timber; little or no tree husbandry; and the lack of regeneration of the trees.

Preface

*I*t would be difficult to over-emphasize the importance of woodland in the lives of our ancestors. To the communities of pre-Industrial times woodland and its many products were a basic need in the struggle for survival. Moreover, our rich cultural heritage owes much to the presence of woodland, even if in many cases this is rooted in the folklore of the distant past.

Since the middle of the 18th century, a mere 250 years or so ago, there has taken place a fundamental change in the role of wood. Coal, oil and gas have all but replaced it as a source of heat. Cheap metals and a huge range of oil-based, 'man-made' materials have become dominant in the construction industries. Plastics have been developed which both look and feel like wood and very often are designed to hide the fact that what lies beneath is no longer *real* wood.

The economics which lie behind these changes can readily be detected on the local landscape. Some Leicestershire woods have occupied all or part of their present sites continuously for long periods. A few have survived in spite of change rather than because of it. In such cases successive generations of owners who found their woods unprofitable, put them to other purposes or simply neglected them. But by and large the development of the woodlands of Leicestershire and Rutland has reflected accurately the changing economic effects of supply and demand, grants and subsidies, import and export policies, investment, taxation, technological innovation and the like.

At the same time woodland has had to compete with other forms of land use which have been subject to much the same forces. In Leicestershire and Rutland one thinks particularly of water supply, mining and quarrying, road building, railway construction and urban growth. Clearly the underlying geology, the nature of the topography and the soils together with the central position of the two counties in the island of Britain, are also major factors in the development of the landscape, especially in modern times.

Yet the role of woodland in the lives of the people in the second half of the 20th century is still changing. Very few indeed make a living from growing, processing or selling wood, especially locally produced wood, but more and more of us have come to value local woodlands for other reasons. As the area of countryside yearly shrinks under a carpet of tarmac and concrete, so demand for access to what remains grows. Landowners and local people are called upon to share their local woodlands with ramblers, sportsmen, naturalists and others escaping from urban areas.

However one may view other aspects of our rapidly changing local landscape, the authors see the position of wildlife habitats, especially woodlands, as at crisis point. There is an urgent need for radical re-assessment of what remains of our woodland heritage if future generations are to enjoy the legacy received by the present one.

We have written this book as a modest contribution to the debate by offering an introduction to an understanding of the development and state of our present woodlands. The aims have been to produce a broad outline against which detailed studies may be seen in better perspective. We have not attempted to comment on all aspects of the subject. The reader will find no references to trees in gardens, in private collections, or in municipal parks. We hope these omissions will be seized upon and developed by others.

Although the scope of this book includes all parts of the present (1994) county of Leicestershire we are very aware that coverage for Rutland, which at the time of writing, is a district within Leicestershire, may be considered less than satisfactory. Throughout the text when we speak of Leicestershire or of Rutland we are referring to the two counties as they existed on the eve of the 1974 local government boundary changes. References to the contrary are, we hope, clearly indicated.

Common names of plant species have followed Stace's *New Flora of the British Isles* (1991) throughout the book. The scientific names and some of the more familiar local names are included in appendix three.

This book is intended for anyone with a concern for the countryside and its wildlife. Those who find the paraphernalia of notes and references annoying or unnecessary may have little need to consult the information on the last few pages. However, we have thought it worthwhile to give details of our sources and amplifications of certain points by providing the necessary sections at the close. In so doing we hope others may feel moved to continue or expand our efforts with their own research.

Acknowledgements

*T*hanks are due to many who have assisted in making this book possible. A large number of people have generously supplied material, including Dr Barrie Cox, John Crocker, Pat and Ian Evans, Stephen Grover, Fred Hartley, Derek Lott, David Ramsey and Stephen Woodward. We are grateful to John Crocker, Peter Gamble, Peter Liddle and John Ward for reading and commenting on the text in part or whole. Thanks are due to the people who drew the originals of various of the maps, and to Robin Stevenson, who redrew them all specifically for this book. We are also indebted to the many landowners, whose permission for access to private woods enabled much invaluable research to be carried out.

Many thanks to Meg Williams for the drawings in figures 1.6, 5.3, 11.8, and 11.9. The photographs are in the main by the authors. The following people and institutions also supplied pictures, for which grateful thanks are given:—

John Tinning — Cover picture, figures 11.3 and 14.2
National Gallery, London — Frontispiece
Peter Gamble — Figure 1.10
SMR, Northamptonshire County Council — Figure 2.2
Bibliotèque Nationale, Paris — Figure 5.2
Leicestershire Museums Service — Figures 7.6 and 13.17
John Crocker — Figure 8.5
Tom Townsend — Figure 10.5
John Shields — Figure 13.3

Chapter One

Introduction to Woodland

Woodland of one sort or another is the natural climax vegetation of much of lowland England including Leicestershire and Rutland. The woodland we have today in both nature and quantity is however far from natural; rather it is the result of man's varied activities and influences over several thousand years. The dynamic nature of vegetation change in a world without man can readily be observed in overgrown gardens, derelict building sites and even 'set aside' fields. Without purposeful and continued human intervention our living landscape, and the nature of the communities which compose it, would take on a much less varied form. By ploughing, cutting, fencing, grazing, burning, draining and liming, generations of our ancestors have manipulated natural processes to meet their particular needs. Thus purely 'natural' communities have been destroyed, modified, transformed, enriched and degraded on both a local and national scale.

The landscape of pre-Industrial England exhibited five basic elements for the survival of its human inhabitants: ploughland, grazing land, woodland, meadow and waste. The first four met specific needs. The waste in most cases, far from being of little value, usually represented a potential or under-used resource for the others. As human needs changed, effort was expended to transform one land use to another. Ploughland could be left to 'tumble down' for grazing, pasture could be ploughed and sown with crops, whilst trees could be felled and their stumps grubbed up for the same purpose. Grazing of stock in woodland was an important aspect of human survival. Meadows, which chiefly provided the grass and hay to feed the plough oxen, could also be used

Figures 1.1 and 1.2
Over the centuries woodland products have been put to many uses, to suit the needs of the time. Above, using simple tools, oak poles are being split to make, for example, the kind of gate shown right. Woodland was a primary resource, and the demand for wood, far from causing its decline through felling, was more often the driving force in its conservation.

IPM of William de Ferrers of Groby, 1288[1]

The jurors ... say that there are at Groby in demesne [land farmed by the lord William] 200 acres of arable land, and at Burgh [Ratby], which is a member of Groby, 4 acres of arable land, of which each acre is extended [valued] at 6d. Sum £9

There are ... 15 acres of meadow [valued at] 30s; and a piece of meadow called Leyfield [valued at] 40s

There is a park at Groby with pasture and pannage worth 66s.8d. yearly, and the underwood of the park 6s.8d.

There is a certain park at Bradgate with herbage, pannage and underwood, worth 40s. yearly. There is a certain foreign [distant] wood in the forest of Charnwood the pasture of which is common, worth 35s.

Rents in the forest of Charnwood of the new assarts [waste taken into cultivation] are worth £7-6s-4d.

IPM of William de Ferrers of Groby, 1445[1]

The jurors say ... there are [at Groby] 300 acres of arable land, each acre, when sown, 2d yearly, of which 100 acres lie fallow this year, and worth nothing because it is common.

There are 24 acres of meadow, worth 16s a year at 8d. per acre. There are two parks [i.e. Groby and Bradgate] worth 6s. a year, besides the keep of the beasts; one close of pasture called 'Le Fold' [i.e. Leyfield] worth 13s.4d.

There is a pasture called Stywordsheyre [Stewards Hey] worth 10s. yearly and they say the underwood is worth 3s.4d. a year.

Figure 1.3

An Inquisition Post Mortem (IPM) was an enquiry, following the death of one of the king's tenants-in-chief, into the land holdings and other sources of profit for which he held responsibilty. Shown here are edited extracts of the IPMs of two of the lords of the manor of Groby.

The first William Ferrers lived at a time when the human population of Leicestershire had reached probably its highest point in the middle ages. The pressure to increase food production is indicated by the rents from new assarts [land cleared for agriculture] in Charnwood Forest. Such areas represent movements into the manorial waste in the search for land to plough. Note the high value of the meadow and woodland.

The second William Ferrers, five generations later, died about a century after the Black Death had first ravaged the population of England. Clearly this manorial economy was taking a long time to recover. Note the fall in the value of arable land and even that of meadow. The two parks were barely paying their way and apparently there was little sold from the woodland, probably because there were too few buyers to warrant proper husbandry.

The Black Death and its aftermath must have had a considerable impact on our local woodland, yet it is only from records such as these, inadequate though they are, that we can even begin to suggest what these changes in the local woodland (illustrated in Figure 1.4) might have been.

by sheep and cows. Pigs were driven to woodland in Autumn to feed on acorns and beech mast. *Waste* was usually, but not always, poor land and its development was undertaken when the demands of the human population for one or more commodities outstripped supply from elsewhere.

Woodlands and their products met a wide variety of our ancestors' needs. *Timber,* the whole or part of large trees, was needed for large domestic buildings, castles, churches and cathedrals and bridges. Demand for it varied both in time and space and maintaining a supply was seen as a matter of long-term planning. Wood, on the other hand, was the smaller stuff and was needed for constructing more modest dwellings, for fences, agricultural and household implements and for fire wood. Here the demand was relatively constant and predictable and it was produced by a regular cycle of cropping.

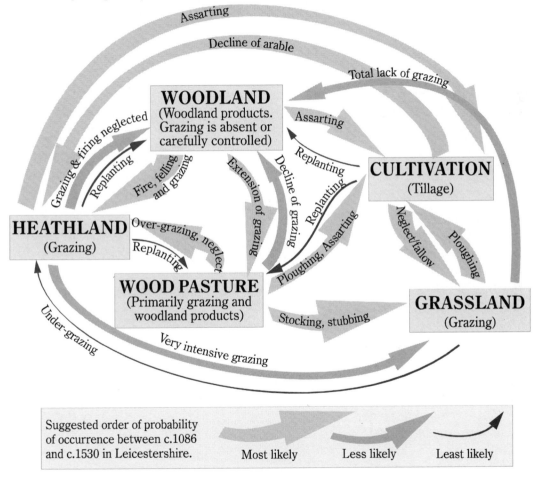

Figure 1.4
Changes between five elements of the medieval landscape.
The landscape of Leicestershire and Rutland has always been a place of change.
The diagram shows how agricultural practices influenced types of habitat in
North-West Leicestershire during the early middle ages.

Figure 1.5
The ridges and furrows of what was once ploughland can be seen crossing this woodland path.

Provision for a supply of both timber and wood was achieved by a number of methods known collectively as *'woodsmanship'*. This relies on the fact that when most British species of deciduous tree are cut near ground level they are not killed, but re-grow vigorously, producing numerous shoots called *poles*, from the stump or *stool*. Growth in subsequent seasons sees these poles develop to a point where they are deemed ready for cutting. This period of growth is usually any time between 7 and 20 years. Such management has been used by man since pre-historic times, and is known as *coppicing*. In practice, blocks of woodland, or *panels,* were cut in rotation so that every year would bring its harvest of poles. Within each panel single stemmed trees, or *maidens,* were usually left to mature into *standards.* Such a

Natural tree shape.
(Parkland specimen)

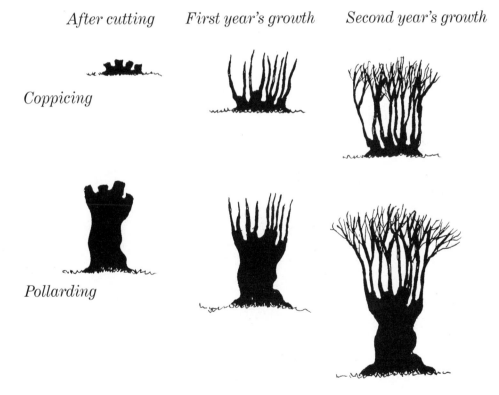

After cutting   First year's growth   Second year's growth

Coppicing

Pollarding

Figure 1.6
Coppice and pollard growth patterns

Figure 1.7
Ancient coppiced ash tree at Stockerston.
The stool is many centuries old.

system was called coppice-with-standards. In Leicestershire and Rutland oak seems to have been the main species promoted as standards, while many other trees and shrubs were coppiced, including ash, hazel, field maple, and (locally) small-leaved lime.

Newly cut coppice is easily damaged by browsing animals such as deer and cattle, and it was because of this that great efforts were made in Saxon and Medieval times to exclude them from these areas. Deep ditches were dug around the perimeter of the woods, the earth being piled on the woodland side to form massive banks, on top of which wooden poles, or *pales,* were erected. Stock was, however, allowed into the woods to graze on a controlled basis.

In addition to coppicing there was another common means of producing a crop of poles, known as *pollarding.* In this process the tree was cut at a height just above that which a browsing animal could reach — perhaps 8 to 12 feet. The uncut trunk was called the *bolling.* This method was used to manage trees along the edges of woods, in hedges (especially on parish boundaries) and in deer parks. In Leicestershire the tree species most frequently pollarded were ash, oak and willow.

A few species of native broad-leaved trees will, when cut down, throw up new shoots, or *suckers,* from the root system, away from the previous stump. The English and small-leaved elms react in this way, but not the wych elm. Other suckering trees and shrubs include aspen and blackthorn.

Figure 1.8
A timber framed
house at
Diseworth.
A medieval wood
provided a wide
range of sizes of
timber for use in
such a building.

Figure 1.9 The result of 25 years of natural regeneration at Ulverscroft.

As long as supply met demand, the woodland serving a community remained little changed in nature and quantity. Where demand outstripped supply, land was protected from grazers and allowed to revert to woodland by natural means. Where supply exceeded demand woodland was grazed, felled, ploughed or simply abandoned. It is not therefore surprising that the ebb and flow of woodland under this ancient management of woodsmanship has resulted in woodland becoming such an enduring feature of the English landscape, and the perpetuation of its dependent flora and fauna.

The more recent system of producing woodland products, one very largely geared to the demands of the industrial society, is that of *'forestry'*. An area of land is deliberately planted with young trees. Often the planting is of a single species which too frequently is a conifer. At the end of a pre-determined period all the trees are felled, the land is cleared and a new planting is made. This system produces stability of tree cover over a short period, but the nature of the woodland produces a very limited variety of conditions and a very restricted flora and fauna. Certain species of conifers can be particularly disadvantageous to the development of a diverse wildlife.

In recent years various terms have been adopted to describe and account for the appearance and nature of woodland on the landscape. *'Primary'* woodlands, where they exist, are those areas where the nature of the woodland has, for one reason or another, remained substantially unaltered since the establishment of the wildwood. There appears to be no woodland in Leicestershire and Rutland which shows any signs of primary status. Rather, our woodlands are much modified forms of semi-natural vegetation. Moreover, some woodlands in Leicestershire and Rutland are clearly recent or *'secondary'* woodlands, i.e. the trees are growing on land which was once used for another purpose. Woodland which can be shown to have been growing before the year 1600 AD (or is suspected of the same) is known

Figure 1.10
Pale Sedge - Carex pallescens.

as *'ancient'* woodland. In practice one finds that most existing large woodlands in our two counties are a mosaic of pieces of ancient and secondary woodland. Some of the ancient pieces may be very old indeed; much of the secondary woodland may be very new.

The richness or otherwise of the flora and fauna may therefore depend as much on its management over the centuries as on its natural features such as the drainage and soils. Accounting for the origin of the wood requires evidence from many sources. Published local histories, maps of various ages and kinds, estate papers, place name evidence and extant archaeological features all provide potential sources of information from which an overall picture can be gained.

In this book we are concerned with the problems regarding the origins of the flora and fauna and the considerations surrounding its conservation. In the first place one must be aware of the problem of under-recording species, not only those of the lesser known invertebrates but also, in many cases, those of flowering plants. It is all too easy to dismiss a woodland as 'uninteresting' on the basis of an inadequate species list. We are also concerned that we know too little about the rates at which species are able to colonise new habitats, when opportunities to do so arise. Certain spider species appear to show little or no ability in this direction and the same appears to be so with some species of flowering plants. The problem may only be resolved when recording to the level of detail not attempted before is achieved and the data compared with a knowledge of the wood section by section.

Much of the early research into the ecological behaviour of particular woodland species was carried out in East Anglia and Lincolnshire. The picture may well prove to be different in the Midlands and elsewhere. The Pale Sedge, for example, is noted as a woodland species in Eastern England where it is considered as confined to ancient woodland. In Leicestershire and Rutland it is often found away from woodland and, in its woodland stations, is by no means confined to ancient woodland.

Often it is difficult to determine when the presence of a species can be accounted for by an unrecorded and deliberate introduction by human action. Seed from a packet may be scattered or whole plants dug in. Often the action is made with the best of intentions and the worst that happens is that the researcher is left scratching his head. At its worst such action as the planting of the visually attractive rhododendrons may well change for ever the nature of the whole wood along with its flora and fauna.

Chapter Two

Woodland from Pre-history to the End of the Roman Occupation.

*R*esearch during the present century, largely the result of pollen-grain analysis, indicates that the final retreat of the glaciers was well advanced by the year 7500 BC and that Britain became separated from the Continent some two thousand years later. Unfortunately there is little evidence of this nature for Leicestershire or Rutland, which lack the natural lakes and peat bogs which best accumulate pollen. However, recent research using the ancient former river channels of the Soar and Trent suggest that vegetation development in prehistoric times was similar to adjacent regions.[1] The research for Britain as a whole gives clear indications that there have been several distinct post-glacial shifts in climate and vegetation, each giving rise to changes in the nature and extent of woodland. The climate we experience at present is, give or take a few minor but well marked interludes, broadly that which made its appearance some two thousand five hundred years ago. The post-glacial prehistoric forests which became established after the final glacial retreat are often now referred to as the *'wildwood'*.

Accompanying those landscape changes was a period in human culture termed the Mesolithic or Middle Stone Age, which ended about 4500 BC. The local archaeological evidence, mostly in the form of flints and stone tools, which are the

Figure 2.1 Neolithic stone axes. These examples were found in Leicestershire, and could be used to fell even large trees.

chief source of information for the period, is now fast accumulating. The present rate of growth may lead us to modify our present views that the tiny human population was well scattered across the landscape and that individuals were all probably organised in wandering groups which followed the migrating herds of wild grazers. Such a population would have affected only in minor ways the then extensive tree cover and other forms of natural vegetation.

Some time after about 4500 BC there arrived from abroad the knowledge of agricultural techniques which were to produce fundamental changes in human societies and their relationships with local landscapes. The so-called 'Agricultural Revolution' meant that for the first time groups of people could farm on the basis of permanent settlement, could produce surpluses of food and could plan for the future. Simultaneously developed were axes large and strong enough to fell even large trees. Such axes together with scatters of flint tools are being discovered each year. Some areas thus cleared could be kept permanently free of trees by the controlled use of domestic grazers. Such pollen analysis as is available for Leicestershire and Rutland suggests the establishment of some early fixed settlement sites.

Taken as a whole the evidence points to the notion that it was at this time that the most fertile and easily worked areas of the two counties were first cleared of their woodland and other natural vegetation. Indeed it is from this Neolithic period in our history that the decline of the wooded nature of the local countryside can be traced. With their primitive stone tools our ancestors managed to clear much of the *wildwood* to produce a landscape which was noticeably little wooded, even by the standards of the rest of lowland England. As later chapters will show, this set a pattern which has prevailed unbroken to the present day.

The arrival in the British Isles around 2500 BC of the knowledge of metal working gave a powerful new tool to our early ancestors. The Bronze Age in Britain saw a renewed attack on the woodlands and an extension of settlement sites. Those most often appear as crop marks which are visible from the air at various times and from flint scatters discovered by field walking. This was the age of the barrow mounds, the development of recognisable field systems and, outside Leicestershire, the henge monuments. Again, hard evidence for the nature of the woodland in this period is scarce in Leicestershire and Rutland, but it seems increasingly likely that throughout the Bronze Age the area of woodland continued to decline as the human population opened new areas for cultivation, especially in the east.

Figure 2.2
Crop marks at Ketton, Rutland, showing the former presence of various bronze age features, among them ring ditches (bottom right.)

Photograph: SMR, Northamptonshire County Council

Figure 2.3
The Iron Age hill fort earthworks at Burrough Hill.

Some time about the eleventh century BC the culture of the later Bronze Age emerged imperceptibly into that which has become known to archaeologists as the Iron Age. About this time arose the hill forts on the prominent Leicestershire landmarks of Beacon Hill, Breedon Hill, Ratby Bury and Burrough Hill, together with many more modest in size and of lesser significance. It has been suggested that the preservation to the present day of some of these sites can be explained by the presence of former woodland. It may also be the case that this type of settlement was a response to a wooded environment in the first place. Crop mark evidence for the Iron Age provides a firm indication of widespread settlements and enclosures with attendant field systems. The enlargement of a minority of settlements into what we may vaguely recognise as towns was also taking place. Archaeological evidence, including that from air photographs and field walking, suggests that Iron Age Leicestershire was an extensively settled and, by the standards of that time, well exploited landscape and one with very little woodland.

The arrival of the Romans marks the first period of recorded history, although no written evidence survives which describes the nature of the Leicestershire and

Figure 2.4
ROMAN SITES IN LEICESTERSHIRE AND RUTLAND

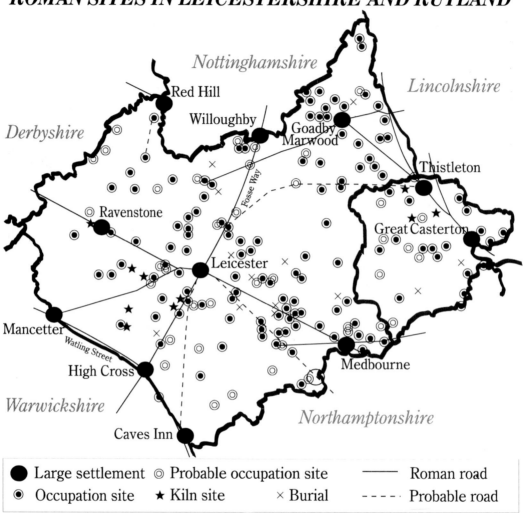

Rutland countryside. On to the pattern of the Iron Age landscape the conquerors imposed and developed their own structures: efficient roads, urban settlements and a range of rural settlements including well known 'villas'.[2] Iron-stone, granite and slate were quarried and iron-working and pottery production were carried on. The organised market economy demanded a ready supply of materials including timber and wood. Liddle has pointed out that the distribution of pottery kiln sites to the west of the Roman City of Leicester supports the idea that the area known in the middle ages as Leicester Forest was probably well wooded before the Romans arrived.[3] Knowledge of Roman Leicestershire from all sources suggests that all the best and much of the poor land was being worked for agricultural or industrial purposes and that the limited quantity of woodland, so important for the development of the economy, formed a well defined and well managed resource.

Chapter Three
Anglo-Saxon and Viking Woodland

*I*n the mid 5th century the Roman Legions withdrew from Britain in response to problems elsewhere in the Empire and four centuries of colonial occupation drew to an end. For many years this retreat has been interpreted by historians as opening the floodgates to violent invasion of Britain by tribes from north-west Europe. However, excavation over the last two and a half decades has suggested that, long before the Romans left, small numbers of those peoples, who were later to be seen as the heathen hordes, had settled and had already become established by peaceful means. In this case, it is believed there was no general 'crash' in social and economic terms since, after a period of adjustment, one system of government replaced another. Whether or not there was a 'gap' between the decline of Roman influence and the establishment of Saxon control remains unclear. Even less clear is the fortune of the woodland of the period.

For the early years of the Saxon settlement in Leicestershire and Rutland the evidence comes mainly from archaeology. Field walking, in particular, has located large numbers of Saxon settlements which otherwise may have escaped notice. Later place name evidence provides some important data about the patterns of settlement, together with clues as to the distribution of certain forms of semi-natural vegetation including woodland. Unfortunately for the two counties, the Anglo-Saxon charters, so abundant and informative for many other parts of England in the middle and late Saxon periods, extend to only a tiny part of Leicestershire and Rutland. The willingness of increasing numbers of students of landscape to go out into the field and study topography in great detail has produced in many cases a better appreciation of the local scene.

Whether or not the Anglo-Saxons came as settlers or conquerors, we can say that in the period from about the middle 5th century to the mid 7th century the newcomers often established themselves on declining or abandoned Roman sites, as indicated by the distribution of Roman coins and pagan Saxon cemeteries. Other settlements were made on entirely new sites and then not always on the most favourable ones. Of these latter, the least successful were destined to be quickly deserted. In places, suitable Roman field systems, including their ancient boundaries, were taken over by the new owners and adopted to their needs. The pattern of this early settlement was ever changing, for there were no nucleated villages in the modern sense. Individual dwellings and those in small groups were scattered and dispersed widely over the landscape, linked only by local social and economic ties.

The Roman economy, which had been fundamentally market-based, collapsed in the first decade of the 5th century and regressed to one resting on subsistence agriculture practised on a very local scale. Thus became established the beginnings of a landscape which was later recognised as the ancient countryside of England. This endured for over a thousand years and came to an end with the Parliamentary

Inclosure Acts of the 18th and 19th centuries. The quantity of woodland and its distribution in Leicestershire and Rutland in these formative years is perhaps best judged by the evidence of later centuries.

For mid Saxon Leicestershire and Rutland, from approximately 650 to 850 AD, the evidence for human activity is more plentiful and relies less on archaeology. This was a time when scattered settlements began to come together to form what today we would recognise as villages with common open fields. Most of these villages have endured to the present, even if their fields have been inclosed at one time or another. Thus was given to the landscape a new form of organisation, together with a relative stability which, as we have seen, had been lacking since Roman times.

PLACE NAME EVIDENCE

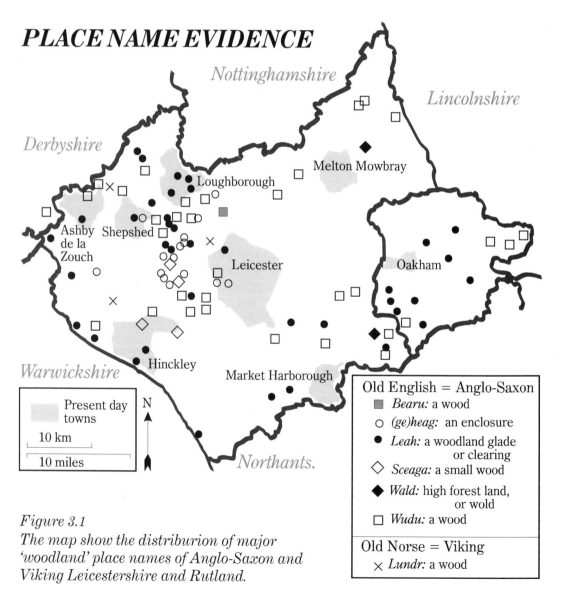

Figure 3.1
The map show the distriburion of major 'woodland' place names of Anglo-Saxon and Viking Leicestershire and Rutland.

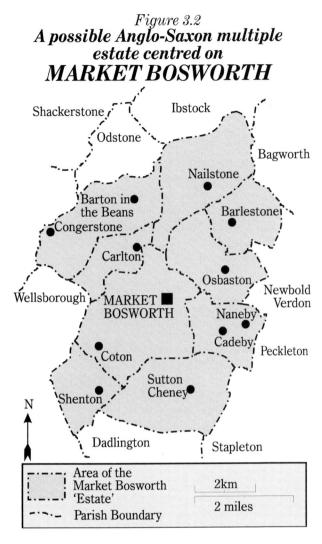

Figure 3.2
A possible Anglo-Saxon multiple estate centred on
MARKET BOSWORTH

Shackerstone

Odstone

Ibstock

Bagworth

Nailstone

Barton in the Beans

Congerstone

Barlestone

Carlton

Osbaston

Newbold Verdon

Wellsborough

MARKET BOSWORTH

Naneby

Cadeby

Peckleton

Coton

Sutton Cheney

Shenton

N

Dadlington

Stapleton

Area of the Market Bosworth 'Estate'

Parish Boundary

2km

2 miles

One possible development was the creation of the so-called *'multiple estates'*. Each of these is thought to have been composed of a block of land formed by what today would be seen as a grouping or 'clumping' of modern parishes. Such estates, it has been suggested, were in the ownership or under the control of one man and were probably self-sufficient in most basic agricultural requirements.[1] The boundaries of these estates were set out formally and often in much detail in charters, although very few of these have survived for the local area. The most studied estate was that at Claybrooke, south-west of Leicester, which was probably disintegrating when the Danes arrived in the late 9th century[2]. Of particular interest is the existence of a block of woodland, *'Leofric's Wood'*, (see figure 3.3) of some 300 acres which adjoined the Watling Street, (now the A5). Here, it seems that the woodland was well defined, well organised and well managed and that it served the needs of a local community that was spread over a wide area. Other multiple estates have been suggested for Hallaton, Lyddington, Market Bosworth, (figure 3.2) Skeffington and the Langtons. Whether or not each had woodland resources is unknown but the believed general shortage of woodland suggests not.

The evidence for woodland from place names supplies local detail which is otherwise lacking[3]. The *'ham'* and *'ton'* suffixes give a general outline of the early settlement pattern in the two counties. The woodland place name elements from Old English, especially *'wold'* (high forest land) as in Prestwold and Wymeswold;[4] *'wudu'* (a wood) as in Woodthorpe and Woodhouse, and *'leah'* (a woodland glade or clearing) as in Burleigh and Charley allows a first recognition of the distinct pattern of woodland which was to endure for another thousand years. This pattern was characterised by three features: first, continued general shortage of woodland in comparison to the rest of lowland England; second, the almost total lack of woodland over wide areas, especially East Leicestershire and south-east Rutland; and third, the concentration of what woodland there was into six main areas where much of it was managed as wood pasture.

These six areas were:-

(i) Charnwood Forest
(ii) the area of west Rutland later known as Leighfield Forest,
(iii) the area west of Leicester later known as Leicester Forest,
(iv) a section of north-west Leicestershire bordering Derbyshire,
(v) a section of south-west Leicestershire bordering Warwickshire,
(vi) a section of northern Rutland.

In 868 AD the Saxon Kingdom of Mercia, which included Leicestershire and
Rutland, was invaded by the Danes after their conquest of much of east and north
eastern England. The evidence for further change on the landscape during the two
centuries before the Norman Conquest (1066) is sparse. It is known that at least a
few new settlements were made but much of their colonising was the occupation of
existing ones. These remarks can be extended to their treatment of woodland
resources and only four examples of the use of the Old Norse 'lundr' (a little

Figure 3.3

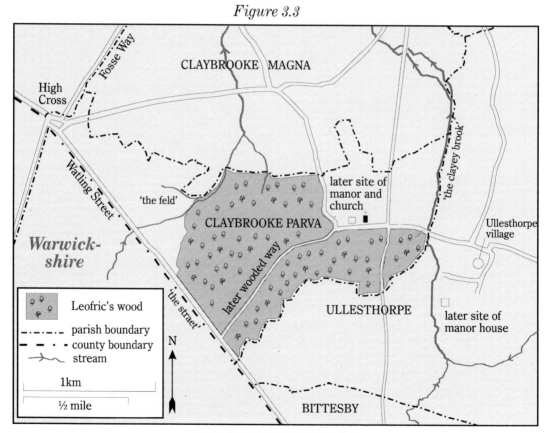

LEOFRIC'S WOOD
as described in the Claybrooke Charter of 962

Figure 3.4
Swithland Wood from the east.

woodland) as in 'Lount' and 'Swithland', are known. In all, the admittedly meagre evidence for Leicestershire and Rutland points to little change to the basic Anglo-Saxon working of the landscape which the Danes found.

The Anglo-Saxons produced and passed to subsequent generations (even to the present) a rich legacy in many forms. What they acquired by settlement and/or conquest and simply handed on little changed, was a landscape in our two counties noticeably lacking in woodland.

Chapter Four

Domesday Woodland

*I*n 1066 Duke William of Normandy lead a successful invasion of England. At Royal command was carried out a survey of the kingdom, and the result, *Domesday Book,* is a description of England in the year 1086. It covers most of the modern country, some of it in great detail. Although the entries include noticeable errors of various kinds they nevertheless provide the first detailed inventory of the English landscape and allow a retrospective assessment of the development of events in late Saxon England. Further, they provide an important background to the factors which were to shape the rural economies of the later middle ages.

The Domesday entries are grouped according to the possessions of the principal landowners and are listed under the individual manors. Some of the manors, such as Barrow, Rothley and Great Bowden, had *'outliers'* or *'dependencies'* which are noted below. Each manorial entry is broken down into several major headings which correspond to the factors upon which the local economy was based. In any study of Domesday, woodland must be seen as one important element of the total manorial or local economy.[1]

The descriptive terms for woodland employed by Domesday Book varied very much over the country. 'Pasture for x swine' is widely used, but says little about the extent or nature of the woodland. The entries for Leicestershire and Rutland are more helpful since nearly all are given in terms of length by breadth and in leagues ($1^1/_2$ miles) by furlongs ($^1/_8$ mile). From the figures it is possible to arrive at a good estimate of the probable extent of each wood and, from entries for woodlands in other parts of England, gain an idea of the nature of such woodland and the use to which it was put.

The folios for Leicestershire have 88 entries for woodland and those for Rutland 29. Map 4.1 shows their distribution plotted according to their manorial listings and relative sizes. Using the middle figure of the procedure outlined by Rackham, the entries for Leicestershire suggest a total of 20,000 acres of woodland and those for Rutland almost 12,000 acres.[2] These figures would suggest that only 3.7% of Leicestershire and 12.3% of Rutland carried woodland. By the standards of much of the rest of late 11th century England these percentages are indeed very low. Such a remarkable shortage of woodland, first detectable at least one thousand years earlier in the Iron Age and possibly originating in Neolithic times, has endured to the late 20th century.

The size of the woodlands in late 11th century Leicestershire varied very much. By far the largest was the one called *'Hereswode',* the 'wood of the multitude', (probably the Danish Army), which lay to the north and west of Leicester. It extended over almost 5,000 acres and in medieval times was destined to become, at least in part, the Chace and later Royal Forest of Leicester.

Next in size were the woods of Groby and Thurcaston which also lay near Leicester and each of which occupied some 1200 acres. Eight other woodlands, each

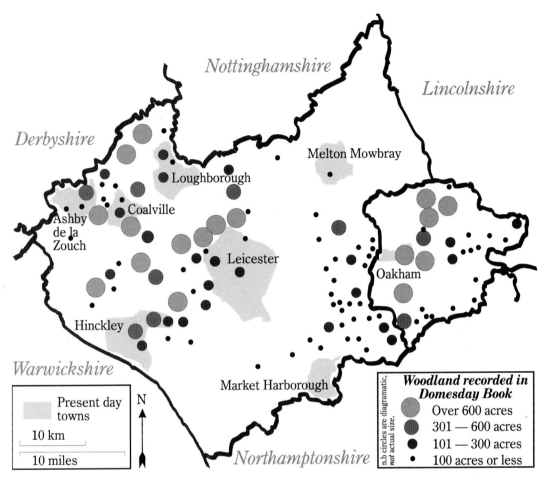

WOODLAND IN DOMESDAY BOOK : 1086

Figure 4.1

*The distribution of woodland as shown by this map broadly indicates the areas
which were least fertile, more difficult to cultivate, and therefore least populated.
The bulk of the population lived in the almost treeless belt across the centre of
the map.*

of some 600 acres, formed the next important group. At once it is clear that the three
largest woodlands accounted for approximately one third of the county's total whilst
the largest eleven accounted for approximately two thirds of this. At the other
extreme, the two smallest woods were the two, each of 3 acres, recorded for East
Norton. Small woodlands of less than 100 acres formed half the county's total, and
of these 20 covered less than 50 acres and 20 less than 20 acres.

In Rutland the largest wood was that recorded for Hambledon which occupied
almost five and a half thousand acres. Other very substantial if much smaller
woodlands were listed for Ridlington (1600 acres), Greetham (900 acres),
Cottesmore (700 acres), Oakham and Overton/Stretton (each 600 acres) and Stoke

Figure 4.2
The Outwoods, near Loughborough – a Domesday Woodland site, seen here from the north-east.

Dry (500 acres) Thus almost half the Rutland total is accounted for by the single largest wood and 87% of the total by that one and the next six largest. The smallest wood was that at Tixover which was stated as being '3 acres' in size. Five other woods were ten acres or less.

Not all Leicestershire 11th century woodlands were mentioned by Domesday Book. Some escaped entry altogether. In the parish of Breedon in the manor of Tonge, for example, 'the wood of Breedon', also known as *'Brunhage Wood'* lay along the border with Derbyshire but was overlooked by the commissioners. Also of interest is the woodland of Charnwood Forest, (See pp.55-61), where the distinctive nature of the soils and the topography together with the records of later centuries suggest the presence of unrecorded woodland.

A second problem arises from the fact that four manors in Leicestershire (Rothley, Melton, Great Bowden and Barrow) and two in Rutland (Oakham and Hambledon) had dependencies or *'outliers'*. These were estates situated at a distance, the economies of which were treated, at least for accounting purposes, as part of that of their capital manor. Of these Leicestershire manors no wood is recorded for any outlier. Either no wood was present or it was included in the manorial 'grand total'. In the case of Barrow, three of the twelve outliers had recorded woodland owned by another person who shared the title 'lord'. Similar situations existed in the other three manors with outliers. If woodlands did exist on the outliers they were probably very small and in any case would have affected only slightly our knowledge of the distribution of woodland rather than the Leicestershire total.

In contrast, the evidence in Rutland for the manors of Oakham and Hambledon points to the presence of woodland in some of the dependencies. Braunston, one of six outliers of Hambledon and mostly on heavy clays, was well wooded in the early middle ages and remained as part of the Forest of Rutland long after the great partial disafforestation of the 15th century. Lyndon, Marthinsthorpe and Manton, three of the others, also probably carried woodland. In the case of Oakham, at least part of the manorial woodland straddled the county boundary so that some of it lay at Knossington in Leicestershire. Whereas these considerations do not affect our view of the total acreage for woodland, they do mean that the distribution of woodland in central and western Rutland remains the subject of some conjecture.

Figure 4.3

Domesday Book Entry for Oakham[1]

Land of The King

In Oakham, five outliers, Church jurisdiction, Queen Edith had 4 carucates of land which were taxable. Land for 16 ploughs.

The King has 2 ploughs at the hall; another 2 ploughs possible.

There are 138 villagers and 19 smallholders who have 37 ploughs. There are 80 acres of meadow.

A priest and a church to which 4 bovates of this land belong.

Woodland pasture 1 league long and $1/2$ a league wide.

The value before 1066 £40.

In the same place Leofnoth had 1 carucate of land which was taxable.

Filcher Malsor has 5 oxen in a plough and 6 acres of meadow.

[Value] before 1066 20s and the same now.

The whole manor, with outliers, 3 leagues long and 1 league and 8 furlongs wide.

In Knossington 3 carucates of land, which belong to the jurisdication of Oakham.

17 Freemen with 6 smallholders have 6 ploughs.

Woodland, 1 furlong long and $1/2$ furlong wide.

Value 20s.

The King has it in lordship.

Leicestershire in 1086 was a county with a slowly rising population and a well exploited agricultural landscape, as judged by the standards of the age. Only the poorest and most difficult soils were not ploughed or grazed and it was to these that most of the woodland was restricted. Of the largest woods, those at Groby, Barrow, Shepshed and Loughborough were accounted for by the Pre-Cambrian outcrops and shallow acid soils of the Charnwood area. The woods of Alton and Ashby stood on the clays which overlie the coal measures. Large areas of Boulder Clay accounted for the sites of the woods of Anstey, Market Bosworth and Bagworth and also the large wooded region which included the woods of Burbage, Barwell and Hinckley.[3]

In Rutland the great bulk of the woodland was situated in the north, the west and (if the problem of the Hambledon outliers is considered) in central Rutland also, where the heavy clays account for much of the surface geology. In contrast, the settlements in the south and east of the county were located on much lighter soils, more favourable to ploughing. Woodland for these manors was almost as scarce as it was in east Leicestershire.

Some of the large woodlands were declining at the time of Domesday Book in favour of tillage. Moreover, in the north-west of Leicestershire a collection of manors recorded a decrease in values and an increase in *'waste'*. This is quite exceptional for Leicestershire and is usually interpreted as an indication of destruction by the conqueror's armies when putting down rebellion in the Midlands.

The locations of the small woodlands to the east of the Fosse in Leicestershire are similarly largely accounted for by the presence of Boulder and Lower Lias Clay, together with considerations of local topography. Most were crowded in the south-east of the county, especially along the border with Rutland. This distribution, together with the fact that the great bulk of Domesday Book woodland was situated to the west of the Fosse meant that a huge swathe of upland east Leicestershire (more than half the county's total area), from Bottesford in the north to Catthorpe in the south was almost totally devoid of woodland.

From this it is interesting to reflect that large numbers of Leicestershire people were faced with a very long walk to their nearest source of woodland products, and a day's journey to and from their nearest large wood.

Chapter Five
Medieval Woodland Areas

*D*omesday Book of 1086 gives a clear indication of the poorly wooded nature of Leicestershire and Rutland. It also reveals the uneven distribution of woodland and its apparent absence from large areas. Even in those areas where it seems there was no shortage, the social and economic changes of the following two centuries resulted in considerable decline in the tree cover. By the beginning of the 13th century the crown and the manorial lords, who between them controlled all major developments on the local landscape, were recognising the need for woodland conservation in one form or another. Attempts at achieving this were made in various ways and with varying degrees of success.

The chief factors accounting for the decline of the woodland were the rise in the human population and the increased demand for land for grazing and ploughing. Domestic stock, managed carefully, could be grazed without the destruction of trees. Provision for ploughland usually meant the total destruction of woodland to the point where roots and stumps were removed. Woodland, once removed, was seldom allowed to regenerate and permanent loss was inevitable.

At an early stage the crown moved to protect its interests by establishing Royal Forests. So extensive did these become that by the reign of Henry III (1216-1272) they covered almost one third of England, although later legislation reduced them severely both in size and number. There were two such Forests in Leicestershire:- Leicester Forest and the Forest of Rutland (Leighfield).

In legal terms a *Royal Forest* was an area of countryside described by definite metes and bounds within which a specific set of rules, the laws of the Forest, regulated the hunting of the *'beasts of the Forest'*. These were the red, fallow and roe deer together with the wild boar. At least in their early days, the Forests were well wooded and they might also contain marsh, pasture and heath. Sometimes whole villages and their field systems were included, and the freedom of the game animals to feed over the croplands resulted in much friction between the crown and local people.

Within the Royal Forests any form of unlicensed or unapproved agricultural practice was prohibited and transgressors were punished. As time went by, the rules were in effect relaxed and fines thus levied were seen as licences to exploit the Forest resources in a

Figure 5.1

The Forest...

'a certain territory of woody grounds and fruitful pastures, priviledged for wild beasts and fouls of the forrest, chase and warren, to rest and abide in, in the safe protection of the King, for his princely delight and pleasure'.

(Manwood 'Laws of the Forest' 1598)

Figure 5.2
The Hunt in medieval times was one of the major forces shaping the landscape.
An illustration from the 14th century French 'Hunting Book' of Gaston Phebus.

closely controlled manner. Such a view allowed for the demand for land from the local population and generated an income for no expenditure. Damaging, cropping and removal of trees were of particular concern and were closely scrutinized by Forest officials. It was, however, these same officials who, lacking proper inspection by uninterested royal masters, were in time responsible for the decline of both Leighfield and Leicester Forests.

Below the crown were the nobles, some of whose wealth rivalled that of the monarch himself. They provided for their love of hunting by the establishment of *chaces.* These were in effect private Forests, although offences committed in them were punishable by Common Law rather than the Forest Laws. They were administered by officials of the lords over whose manors they extended.

In Leicestershire the Forest of Leicester was a chace until 1399 and was ruled with an iron hand by the dukes of Lancaster. Charnwood Forest, although richly endowed with woodland, was always in law a chace, and as such, was controlled by the various lords. For these men Charnwood represented the waste land of their respective manors. Much the same sorts of pressure for exploitation of woodland resources together with measures for its conservation were present here as were present in both Leicester and Leighfield Forests. The subsequent development and fate of the woodland in this chace was quite different from that in the two Forests.

In an effort to ensure a perennial supply of game for hunting, both monarch and nobles established reserves called parks. These were areas of countryside, typically on the edge of a manor and on agriculturally inferior soil, which were surrounded by a *pale*. This consisted of a ditch, a bank and a fence. Parks most often contained woodland which produced an income for the lord and a supply of raw materials for the local community, as well as cover for the deer. In some parks the grazing of domestic animals took place alongside that of the deer. Parks in

Figure 5.3 Beasts of the Forest.

Figure 5.4[2]

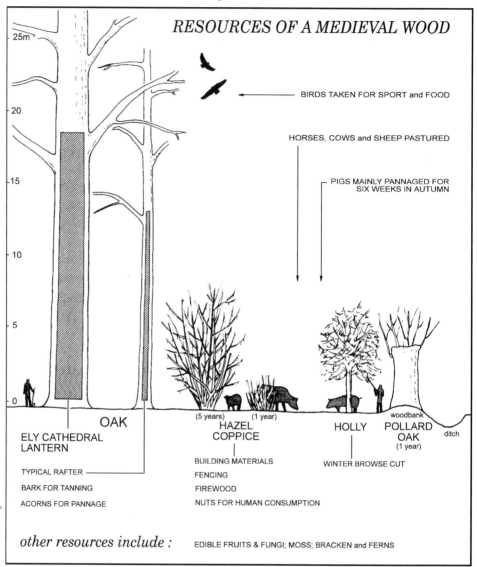

RESOURCES OF A MEDIEVAL WOOD

BIRDS TAKEN FOR SPORT and FOOD

HORSES, COWS and SHEEP PASTURED

PIGS MAINLY PANNAGED FOR
SIX WEEKS IN AUTUMN

OAK
ELY CATHEDRAL
LANTERN

TYPICAL RAFTER
BARK FOR TANNING
ACORNS FOR PANNAGE

(5 years)   (1 year)
HAZEL
COPPICE

BUILDING MATERIALS
FENCING
FIREWOOD
NUTS FOR HUMAN CONSUMPTION

HOLLY

WINTER BROWSE CUT

woodbank
POLLARD   ditch
OAK
(1 year)

other resources include :   EDIBLE FRUITS & FUNGI; MOSS; BRACKEN and FERNS

Leicestershire varied in size from a few acres to the giant park of Whitwick which covered the summit and slopes of Bardon Hill and which extended over 1260 acres. The period of high parking in the county spanned the years 1200-1350. Fifty or so sites are known but few parks survived the social and economic changes which followed the arrival of the Black Death in 1348.[3]

The great mass of the population found little or no time for unproductive leisure. Survival from one year to the next for most people rested on the success of a peasant economy. This centred on the five categories of land use noted earlier, one of which was woodland. The relationship between pasture and woodland was flexible. Certain persons gained or inherited rights of grazing stock over lands which belonged to others. Such rights often extended to woodland, especially where the woodland was on the manorial waste. Thus had arisen, long before the middle ages, the demand for grazing and the need for regulation of the same. These concerns were to have a fundamental role in determining the nature and extent of the woodlands in Leicestershire in medieval times and later.

The major wooded commons of medieval Leicestershire for which any records survive were almost all centred on the great woodlands described in Domesday Book. At both Alton and Bagworth the extensive woodlands were already in an advanced state of decay or were not subject to any serious (or at least successful) attempt at regulating the grazing. As a result, regeneration of trees was prevented, and the woodland passed to a state of treeless heath well before the mid 13th century. In other places manorial regulation was more successful. At Castle Donington, where common grazing extended into Derbyshire, a large portion of the Domesday Book woodland was inclosed in Donington Park. The manors of Barwell, Burbage and Hinckley shared common grazing in the Domesday Book woodlands which occupied the area where the three modern parishes meet. To this day these ancient common grazing rights remain on Burbage Common.[4] At Rothley, the grazing rights and the fortunes of the early wooded area followed much the same pattern as those of Charnwood Forest.

The Forests, chaces and parks offered stability in a changing landscape and the features of many of them long outlived their original purpose. Some of the remnants of these can be seen today; others survive as place names. *'Plain'* as in Rothley Plain, *'lawns'* and *'launde'* as in Launde parish, are all indications of grassy areas between woods, or at least patches of trees. *'Frith'*, as in Glenfield Frith, indicates the woodland on the outside of a Royal Forest, as does *'Purlieu'*, which was woodland partly subject to Forest Law. Place names associated with the loss of trees are: *'assart'*, land won from waste (often woodland in Leicestershire); *'stubbing'* and *'stocking'* (as in Stocken in Rutland), land cleared of trees; and *'breach'*, land broken up for cultivation.

Chapter Six

Leicestershire and Rutland in the Middle Ages

*T*he years 1066 to c.1530 are often referred to as the Middle Ages and were a time of much change in the more wooded parts of Leicestershire and Rutland. For the first century or so of this period there was only a slow increase in the local human population; but this movement gathered pace through the 13th century and reached a peak around the year 1300. Thereafter numbers began to decline and were dramatically reduced after 1348 as a result of repeated outbreaks of the Black Death. Even six generations or so later, at the start of the reign of Henry VIII (1509-1547), numbers had still not regained their pre-Plague levels.[1]

For the century and a half following Domesday Book written records for woodland in Leicestershire and Rutland are virtually non-existent. They remain so until the mid 13th century when detailed manorial records make their appearance. Some of the largest woods recorded by Domesday Book, such as that at Alton (near Coalville), were already under pressure from the demand for more land for tillage, and probably did not survive long into the 12th century. Most of the other large woodlands, e.g. those at Groby and Market Bosworth, were reduced and fragmented during the same period and for similar reasons.

Other substantial woodlands, mostly those of between 200 and 400 acres, also suffered reduction in size. After Domesday Book there is no record of woodland at Stanton or Markfield. At Breedon clearance had reduced the former extensive woodland to isolated patches. Perhaps not surprisingly it was the small woods, especially those east of the Fosse where woodland was in any case scarce, which survived most successfully to the early 13th century. Thereafter any woodland over 50 acres or so had a good chance of continued survival, at least in part, to the early twentieth century.

Thus it was largely unrecorded human activity in these early years of the middle ages which reduced the large woodlands of Anglo-Saxon Leicestershire and which completed the pattern of small, discrete woodlands which in essence, although not necessarily in detail, endured to the mid 17th Century and in part to the present century.

Of particular importance to the management of woodland on the medieval landscape of Leicestershire (and to a lesser extent Rutland) was the foundation of upwards of a dozen monastic houses during the 12th and early 13th centuries. Many of these were located in places where there was still no shortage of woodland or where endonments included wooded land. There were five such settlements in and around Charnwood Forest alone. At Launde, in east Leicestershire the priory was located within the wooded environs of the Forest of Rutland and at Brooke (also in the Forest of Rutland) the original endowment included about 228 acres of wood.

As a group, the religious houses in Leicestershire and Rutland were to become important as owners and conservers of woodland until the Dissolution of the Monasteries in the 1530s. From the surviving data, crude and incomplete as they are, we may suggest that the 2000 to 2500 acres of woodland they owned represented something approaching five per cent of their total holdings.

The steady rise in demand for food from the expanding human population of 13th century Leicestershire could only be met by an extension of the area of land under the plough. This produced a move into the more marginal areas of both counties, to the heavier clays and to the acid soils of the Pre-Cambrian rocks. Pressure on woodland was now considerable and the records for assarting, (reclamation from the 'waste' – often woodland), are largely confined to Charnwood Forest, Leighfield Forest and Leicester Forest. The wooded areas of the two Royal Forests were protected to a large extent by supervision of the crown. Those on Charnwood were managed with moderate success by the various manorial lords. In all three areas, as elsewhere in the two counties, there was an urgent need for woodland conservation, and it is from the records of the 13th and early 14th

Figure 6.1
The Priory of Launde (just left of centre in this picture) was founded some time before 1125, and lay within the Royal Forest of Leighfield. In 1248, shortly after the Forest was reduced in size, the prior was granted licence to impark. The legacy today of the formerly well wooded environment takes the form of Launde Big (or West) Wood (in the foreground), and Launde Park Wood, seen beyond the open parkland of Launde Park.

*Figure 6.2
An early coal pit
in Southwood,
Ashby-de-la-
Zouch. This is one
of many on this
landscape, where
mining is first
recorded in the
13th century.*

centuries that we recognise by name for the first time many of the individual woodlands which served their local, and also more distant, communities.

The creation of the fifty or so hunting parks in the two counties was to prove an important factor in the conservation of the threatened woodland. By the late 12th century the larger beasts of the chase were confined to the more remote areas of the two counties where there were fewest people. Most parks were created on the edges of their respective manors, which was most often where woodland survived. The link with Domesday Woodland in this respect is often very marked. At Barrow, Breedon, Ashby, Castle Donington, Market Bosworth, Bagworth, Thurcaston, Oakham and Ridlington the creation of the respective parks incorporated part or all of the Domesday Woodland sites. The greatest concentration of parks was in the Charnwood Forest area where the land was poor, where the terrain was very favourable to emparkment and where the woodland was not under Royal control. The legacy of these early hunting parks proved to be an important factor in the survival of woodland in particular, and the development of landscape in general, for many centuries after their decline and abandonment.

By 1086 the majority of the two counties' towns and villages were in existence, although some were not specifically named by Domesday Book which contains many 'silent' entries. During the middle ages, not only did the human population rise and fall in number but there were also important changes in its distribution. No less than sixty-five villages noted by Domesday Book for Leicestershire and about thirteen for Rutland, together with some settlements known only from an odd medieval reference, shrank, were deserted or otherwise disappeared before the year 1400. Depopulation by monastic houses during the years 1125-1350 for the furtherance of sheep farming, depopulation of settlements after the Black Death together with subsequent contraction of farming during the years 1350-1400, and inclosure for pasture and improved arable after 1400 accounted for most of these.[2] Although village decay and abandonment were widely spread across the counties they do not appear to have been related to the fortunes and pattern of contemporary woodland.

The distribution of known medieval woodlands in Leicestershire as drawn from documentary sources is shown on figure 6.4. Although this representation is imperfect, it clearly echoes the distribution of woodland in 1086. In particular it indicates that most woodlands were confined to four areas of the county and confirms that most of the rest had very little woodland at all.

An examination of the woodlands named produces some interesting features. Tracing a particular woodland through the names of successive owners can lead to the identification of its location on the landscape. At Lubbesthorpe 'the wood of Roger la Zouche', first named in 1302 was, in whole or in part, 'the wood of William Hastings' in 1483. Later documentary evidence shows it to have been synonymous with the wood variously known as *'The Hat'* and *'The Thwaite'* and which disappeared shortly after 1630. In a similar way, woodland names have long survived the woods themselves. Talbot Woods at Swannington recall the name of the 13th century lords of the manor although the woods had gone long before the end of the middle ages. Woodlands called le Carre (Frisby) and Le Kerre (Staunton Harold)

Figure 6.3
The site of the former village of Hamilton, on the north-east edge of Leicester.
Never large, and weakened by successive outbreaks of bubonic plague, it was
eventually depopulated in the early 15th century.

LOCATION OF MEDIEVAL WOODLANDS
as described in documentary sources: c.1200 — 1530
(Not including Rutland)

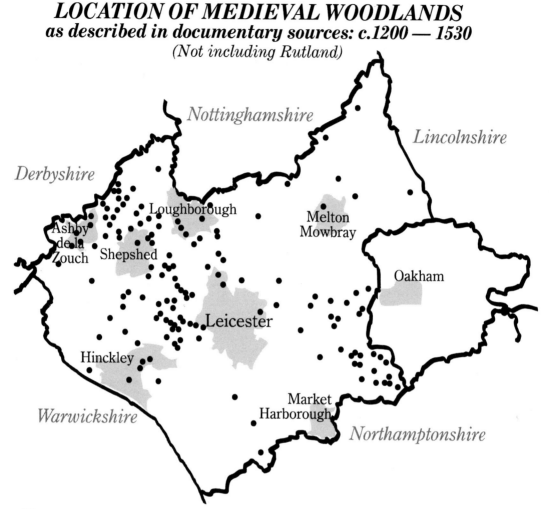

Figure 6.4

Data for this map has been obtained by trawling through a very wide variety of documentary and published sources. Each dot represents one named woodland and has been plotted according to the manor or parish for which it is noted. The exact location of many woods remains a mystery. Moreover, the size of many of our local woods is seldom stated with precision, so that the dots represent woods of widely different extent. Where a woodland site can be recognised under different names in different ages, only one dot has been used. It should be noted that not all of the woodlands shown existed together at any one time. The value of this map, imperfect though it is, is firstly that it echoes Domesday Book in indicating the highly localised nature of the woodland of Leicestershire, and secondly that it demonstrates that large areas of the county were more or less devoid of woodland

were in wet places and were alderwood by streams. 'South Wood Park' (Market Bosworth) and 'le Park' (Great Easton) are self-explanatory. 'Swinland' (Cold Newton), 'Swinhagh' (Hallaton) and 'Swythenhul' (Kirby Muxloe) all accommodated pigs at one time or another, whilst 'Stocking Wood' (Thurmaston) and 'Breche Wood' (Blaston) both speak of woodland destruction and clearance.[3]

The small woods in the more fertile parts of Leicestershire and Rutland were run on the usual system of coppice-with-standards, where the entry of livestock was carefully controlled or avoided altogether. Such woods were usually the sole property of the lord (or lords) of the manor. Common rights to wood and to grazing may or may not have been enjoyed by the tenants as local custom dictated. In the less fertile areas the larger woods, for example those at Burbage, Great Easton and Croxton Kerrial, were part of a complex and often extensive system of land management involving inter-commoning and common grazing on heathland, and moorland as well as in woodland. At Castle Donington the system extended across the border with Derbyshire and covered several hundred acres. Towards the end of the middle ages, 'common' land became synonymous with treeless land. Swannington Common, Ashby Woulds, and the heaths at Saltby, Newbold Verdon and Bagworth were all treeless. In Charnwood Forest, the greatest common of all, the common grazing was so intense that regeneration ceased altogether in the unfenced areas.

It is difficult to assess how much woodland there was in the medieval counties since the documentary record for the period is so unsatisfactory. We are left to make broad inferences from the records of Domesday Book and those of later centuries. From these it seems very likely that there was less woodland present at the end of the period than there had been at the beginning and that there was little, if any, more than was to exist in Tudor and early Stuart times.

Figure 6.5 (overleaf)
A boundary pollard.
Trees growing on the edge of a wood, such as this one at Prior's Coppice, were often pollarded in historic times. This process produced a crop of wood which was safely out of reach of browsing animals in the adjacent fields. Pollards also sometimes served as parish boundary markers, which is the case in this instance.

Chapter Seven
The Three Forests

Leicester Forest

*A*t the time of Domesday Book the wooded area, then described as 'the wood of the multitude' extended in a broad sweep from Peckleton in the south-west to Anstey in the north-east and occupied in total a little over 5000 modern acres. In places the tree cover was thick and continuous. Certain parts – the *'reserved'* areas of later records – were maintained as places for the production of timber and underwood or as sanctuaries for the deer. Other parks, especially those which later became known as the *'friths'*, were places where the people of Leicester collected wood. In the areas of lawn – the 'spaces between the trees' – the open grassland allowed local people to exercise their long-held rights to graze domestic stock.

From Hugh de Grantesmaisnil, the original grantee, the Forest passed to successive earls of Leicester who in turn exercised a firm control over the area's development. Early grants from the Forest to individuals and institutions included one by Simon de Montfort to Leicester Abbey of some 320 acres of his woods adjoining the Abbey's lands. (see figure 7.2)[1] Similar enclosures took place at Gilroes and at Basset House, on the southern edge of the Forest. Grants of wooded land for conversion to pasture or arable were also made. In 1316 for example, the Abbot of

Figure 7.1
An ancient oak at the Gynsills, Anstey.
It is hardly possible to guess the age of this specimen. As much a mystery is the nature of the inclosure in which it once stood. It may be the last survivor of the Royal Forest.

Figure 7.2

Grant of Woodland to the Abbey of Leicester 1252

Inspeximus and confirmation of a charter, whereby Simon de Monte Forti, earl of Leicester, gave to the church of St. Mary de la Pre, Leicester, and the canons regular there, three hundred and twenty acres of land and wood in his forest called 'Defensa' by Leicester with all things there growing; which land lies from the road to Anstey to Dalesike crossways, and from Dalesike beyond Sterkeshull to Oldefield crossways upon the path from Cropston as shown by the metes and bounds, and from Oldefield round by the field of Belgrave, and by the field of the said canons to the road to Anstey; and all Cleyhegges with all things there growing; to be held by the said canons... so that they may enclose the same with a dike and cultivate it or make such profit thereof as they will, as free of all service, demand, suits or customs... saving to the grantor his venison...

*Witnesses, Sir Stephen de Segrave and
    eleven others.*

from the Calendar of Charter Rolls 1226 - 1257

Leicester Abbey granted William de Herle permission 'to enclose his wood of Kirby [Muxloe] called Whatecroft'.[2]

In spite of the tight control by the Beaumont earls, the wooded nature of the area declined and by the middle of the 13th century it became necessary to take measures to conserve resources. The best of the woodlands were gradually inclosed, the principal ones being shown on figure 7.5.[3] A second measure was the establishment of the hunting parks. These primarily safeguarded the deer but they also contained important woodland reserves.

The attachment of the Duchy Estates to the crown lands in 1399 saw the waning of royal interest in Leicester Forest. Changing social and economic circumstances meant it was easier for the monarch to place the administration of royal areas in the hands of powerful local magnates such as the Hastings or the Greys. Throughout the 15th and 16th centuries the neglect, over-exploitation and downright plunder produced a steady decline of some of the best woodland. By 1523 it was remarked that the royal woodland in the Forest 'is all decay and wasting and the woods that are left there by grown on other men's grounds'.[4]

Uncontrolled sheep grazing was a serious problem, as was the unlicensed felling and carting away of thorns. Moreover, the remaining deer competed with the commoners' cattle and with the rabbits from the four local warrens. The commoners in turn complained that the king's deer spoilt their crops and deprived them of their livings.

A survey of 1606 listed the woodlands and the trees which still remained to the king, (see figure 7.3), but this only served to highlight the great decline which had taken place.[5] By 1628 the point of no return had been reached. King Charles, short of money and lacking any real interest in this part of the royal estate, sanctioned the disafforestation of what was left of Leicester Forest. The deer were killed, the woodland felled and the land sold and turned over to agriculture by the new owners.

Figure 7.3

Survey of the Woods belonging to the Duchy of Lancaster in Leicester Forest 1606[5]

1. In the station or walk of George Cater, one of his majesty's rangers in the said forest, which [walk] contains 300 acres of ground there are 2300 of young oaks called sapplings and of others, 1000 of them worth 2s a piece, 500 worth 12d and 800 worth 6d .

2. In the same walk 200 young oaks worth 2s 6d and 120 worth 12d.

3. In the same walk 40 dodderells [ancient decaying trees] worth 2s a tree.

1. In the station of John Cater, one of his majesty's rangers in the same forest [there are] 450 acres of ground [with] 180 timber trees of oak [worth] 5s a tree.

2. In the same walk 1200 young oaks or sapplings at 3s 4d a tree.

3. Also 1200 oak sapplings at 2s 6d a tree.

4. Also 700 sapling oaks at 8d a tree.

5. Also 300 sapling oaks at 12d a tree.

6. Also 100 ashes at 12d a tree.

7. Also 60 ashes at 18d a tree.

8. Also 40 dodderells [the species is not recorded] at 2s a tree.

> Currency Conversion:−
> 6d = $2^1/_2$p
> 12d = 1 shilling = 5p
> 2s6d = $12^1/_2$p

Figure 7.4

Presentment of Spoil and Waste in Leicester Forest, 1606[6]

We [the jurors] present Walter Hastings for cutting wood in the forest called Narborowes [Narborough] Shorttress ... and in Narborowes Wood ... also for cutting down of a thicket of the forest joining to a lane called Peartree Lane and for holding the same enclosed for his own use ... and for maintaining purpresture [encroachment] upon the forest at Frith Lane Gate by a lodge and a warren of conies [rabbits] to the great oppression of the commons there and the utter exiling of his Majesty's game ... and another warren of conies which does spread and feed over 200 acres of ground at least.

We do present ... Sir Henry Hastings of Braunstone for cutting down the forest wood called Barn to the number of 500 trees and if there is not a restraint in [a] short time there will be nothing left to shroud the deer in.

Likewise we do present Sir George Manners for cutting down the vert [vegetation] of the forest in a place called Hatte ... and for enclosing the same and cutting the same for his own use (the value of the ground is 30 acres).

We present Messrs Thomas and John Gardner of Enderby for cutting down the forest wood in a place called Thwaite and for keeping the same enclosed and converting [it] to sheep pasture to the value of 80 acres ... value £3 per acre.

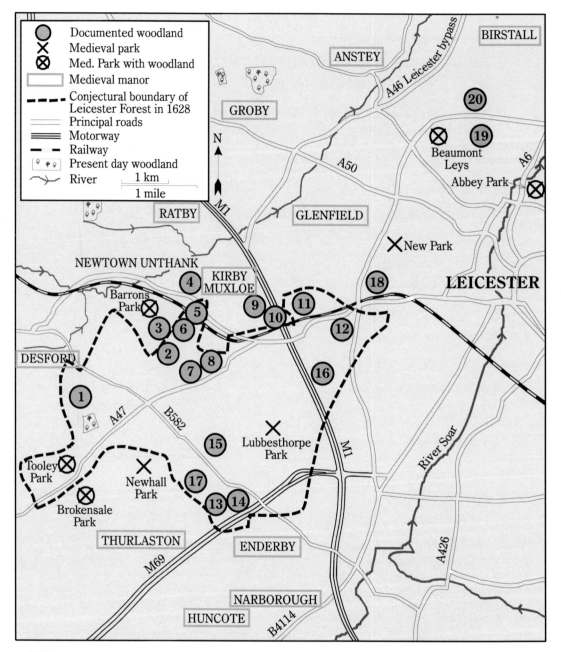

THE MEDIEVAL WOODLANDS OF LEICESTER FOREST

Figure 7.5[3] (See opposite for the key to woodland names.) The location of each woodland is only approximate, determined through field work and a large number of documentary sources. Some woods may have adjoined one another, and it should not be supposed that all the woods were present at any one time. The landscape of even a Royal Forest was subject to social and economic change.

The Medieval Woodlands of Leicester Forest

Map No. Wood name	Earliest known name and year
In Kirby Muxloe	
1. Le Hore	Le Gores 1314
2. Prior's Wood	Prior Wood 1372
3. Brickman's Hill and Shilton Wood	Britmundshul 1281
	Shilton Wood 1372
4. Gullet Wood	Le Golet 1310
5. Swineshill	Swythenhull 1345
6. Pakeman's Wood	Pakeman's Wood 1247
7. Glouchief	Glouchief 1314
8. Sallows	le Salunes 1299
9. Scrathawe	Scrathawe 1462
10. Wheatcroft	Watecroft 1234
In Braunstone	
11. Kings Wood	Kings Wood 1364
12. Barnho	Wood of Braunstone 1250
In Lubbesthorpe	
13. Thwaite	Wood of Roger la Zouche 1302
In Narborough	
14. Narborough Short Trees	Narborough Short Trees 1373
15. Narborough Wood	Northburgh Wode 1373
In Huncote	
16. Wood of Huncote	Wood of Huncote 1319
In Thurlaston	
17. Turville Wood	Turville Wood 1309
18. Doveland	Doveland c.1252
19. Stocking Wood	Storkeshull 1252
In Beaumont Leys	
20. Beaumont Wood	Beaumont Wood 14th C.

The Parks of Leicester Forest

*T*ooley Park was an early creation of the earls of Leicester at Earl Shilton and adjoined the Forest. During the 13th and 14th centuries it contained valuable woodland and pasture and was enclosed with the traditional wooden pale. In 1526 it extended over about 450 acres when wood was worth 12d a load and underwood 6d.[7] As late as 1606 it contained 5,800 ashes, 4,800 young oaks, 180 timber trees and 112 dotterell [decaying] trees.[8] In 1626 it held 200 deer.[9] After its sale by the Duchy in 1627, much of the timber disappeared to be replaced in the following century by the ornamental spinneys we see today.

*B*arn Park alias Barrons Park, on the edge of Desford manor, was another inclosure from the Forest. During the 14th century it contained much woodland.[10] In 1399 the cost of repairing the pale came to 58s-10½d and the income from faggots sold was £6-5s-4d.[11] By 1526 an acre of the best woodland produced 72 loads of oak and ash timber worth £4-15s together with three loads of underwood at 8d a load.[12] After 1628 the park passed out of the Duchy and by 1680 its woodland had been converted to pasture and tillage. Its eastern end is the site of a recent housing development.

*F*rith Park at Leicester was in 1297 held by Edmund, earl of Lancaster[13] and in 1444 was bestowed by Henry IV on his intended wife.[14] The area was well wooded and part at least formed an important source of supply of woodland products for the people of Leicester. In 1524 it was well stocked with deer and there was 'great plenty of wood called old stand but little timber or none.'[15] Two years later the Frith, now removed from the Forest, was the site of Henry VIII's New Park.[16] But its life as a hunting park was short. By 1606 it had been divided and drained to produce pasture for 1000 sheep.[17] It is now the site of New Parks housing estate.

*T*he area known as *Beaumont Leys* passed in the 12th century from the earls of Leicester to the Knights Templar and then to the Knights Hospitaler. It was a well wooded area and had contained deer long before 1507 when George Hastings was described as 'keeper of Beaumont Lees'.[18] In 1524 the park was still part of the Duchy of Lancaster,[19] and it contained many deer and a great number of 'young oak timber by estimate of 80 years growth'.[20] Two years later it was divided into two parts,[21] and when Leland visited it in the 1530s much had been converted to pasture. By the beginning of the 17th century its 340 acres contained only '380 timber trees worth 10s each, 680 dotted oaks at 4s each and 80 saplings at 2s'.[22]

*L*ubbesthorpe Park is known from a lone record of 1361 and it extended over a few acres.[23] It is remembered as a group of field names and part of its perimeter is indicated by short stretches of bank and ditch. The site is north-west of Abbey Farm.

*B*rokensale Park is also known from one record, that of 1279 when Ralph Turville held it for the earl of Leicester. The site is about 2 miles west of Thurlaston.[24]

*N*ewhall Park at Normanton was created by Sir William Turville in the reign of Henry VIII.[25] It contained deer and presumably woodland but by 1564 it had been disparked.[26] It is now farmland.

*T*he abbot and convent of *St. Mary de Pratis* had a park adjoining their *Abbey*, now Leicester's Abbey Park. Nothing is known of its early history but in 1551, after the Dissolution, and its passing into lay hands, it still contained deer and woodland.[27]

The Forest of Rutland

*T*he Forest of Rutland, later known as Leighfield Forest, was created by Henry I shortly after the year 1100.[28] In its early days it occupied the southern half of the county of Rutland together with a narrow and adjacent strip of Leicestershire. As a hunting area the Forest took advantage of the rich legacy of Domesday woodland. In 1235 the Leicestershire portion was disafforested[29] and in 1299 much of the eastern half of Rutland too was released from the Forest laws.

The early Forest contained many villages with their field systems, roads and other features which together presented serious handicaps to successful Forest administration. The extensive woodland, though, lay in discrete entities, most of them fenced to discourage the deer from grazing and to regulate domestic stock. The rights of the King and those of the local people were overseen by Forest officers. During the reigns of strong monarchs, such as Henry III, Forest law was strictly enforced; but weak monarchs such as Stephen and John lost their grip on the royal preserves and both venison and vert suffered at the hands of local people.

Some of the problems of maladministration lay with the Royal Officers themselves. Local officials were corrupt and incompetent. One forester ran a private piggery of no fewer than 300 animals in the Forest 'to the great injury of the King's deer'[30]. For their part, monarchs were often too free with gifts of deer and oaks to their favourites or to worthy causes, and granted assarting rights with too little thought for their probable long term effects.

At some time in the middle ages the area of the Royal Forest contracted until it occupied only a small part of the western edge of Rutland, centred on the manor of Leighfield. In Elizabeth's reign it, and the royal park of Ridlington, contained thirty three distinct woodlands totalling 1,060½ acres.[31] The largest was 75 acres and the smallest 3 acres (see figure 7.7). Oak and field maple were the chief tree species with a typical shrub layer of hazel and thorns. Some of the oaks in particular were then estimated to be 300 years old, but everywhere there was a noticeable shortage of underwood.[32]

In the late 16th century Royal interests in the area were managed by various members of the Hastings family of Ashby-de-la-Zouch. The Royal hunting lodge at Leighfield was maintained for the monarch but seldom used by her since she preferred to follow the chace in her more favoured parks.

Figure 7.6
Henry Hastings (1539 – 95),
3rd earl of Huntingdon and
Forester of Leighfield Forest.

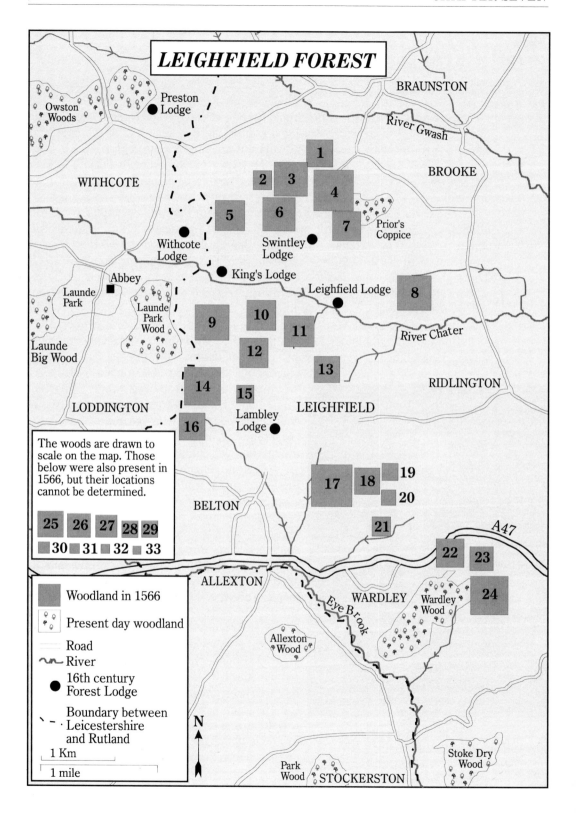

LEIGHFIELD FOREST

The woods are drawn to scale on the map. Those below were also present in 1566, but their locations cannot be determined.

25 26 27 28 29
30 31 32 33

Woodland in 1566

Present day woodland

Road

River

16th century Forest Lodge

Boundary between Leicestershire and Rutland

1 Km

1 mile

Figure 7.7 (opposite, see below for the key to woodland names).
Leighfield Forest according to an inquisition of 1566 conducted at the
queen's command by Sir James Harrington and others. The forest was
divided into three bailiwicks, or administrative areas: Braunston bailiwick
covering the northern section; 'the park' [of Ridlington] bailiwick occupying
the central section; and Beaumont bailiwick in the south.
The earl of Huntingdon was the warden 'by inheritance' and Edward
Hastings was his 'Leyftenant'.
The areas of the individual woods are drawn to the same scale as the map,
but their locations are only approximate. The sources are noted in the
references.

Key to the Woods of Leighfield Forest

No.	Name	Area (acres)	No.	Name	Area
1	Brawnston Thyn	32	17	Lostokes	75
2	Huntes Wood	16	18	Palewell Quarter	30
3	Oliver	50	19	Hawthornes Quarter	12
4	Brawnston Syde	72	20	Hawthorne Quarter	10
5	Wolfett	40	21	Hanging Hawthorne	16
6	Todeholes	49	22	Ffyne Oak Quarter	35
7	Swyncke Cliffe	38	23	Castell Hills and Harmesley	25
8	Stockwood	53	24	Monkeshill	65
9	Betillwell	54	25	Coneygrehills	30
10	Kinge Okehill	40	26	Belton Quarter	25
11	Fayre Okehill	43	27	Half Acre Quarter	22
12	Hamyhille	37	28	Catwell Quarter	13
13	Ffrewoode	30	29	Pynfold Quarter	13
14	Coltlees	72	30	Lodge Quarter	6
15	Lamley	14	31	The Earl's Wood	4.5
16	Watter Lees	32	32	Monkeswood	4
			33	The Earl's Wood in Stockhorn	3
				Total	1060.5

A survey of the Royal Forest in 1609 noted that it contained 9281 trees. These comprised 6955 timber oaks worth £826-0s-5d and 2326 decayed oaks 'fit for fuel' worth £36-1s-4d. In 'Beaumont Park', the area south of the present Wardley Wood, there were no fewer than 2066 timber oaks worth £1126-13s and 99 'fuel oaks' worth £29-12s.[33]

Thirteen years later Leighfield Forest was noted as containing 17 discrete wooded areas totalling 1230 acres;[34] but it is clear that not all these carried the same level of tree cover as indicated by the earlier survey. The Royal Forest was now almost entirely confined to the modern parishes of Leighfield, Wardley and

WESTERN RUTLAND
in 1611

Figure 7.8 (opposite)
John Speed's map of Rutland, 1611, represents the first major attempt to
map the ancient parks and woodlands of the county with any regard for
accuracy. The general pattern of the distribution of woodland at the time of
Domesday Book (1086) is still clearly evident on this ancient map.

The Rutland Eyre, AD 1269

Of the extortion of Peter de Neville

It is presented and proved by the verderers, regarders and twelve as well
knights as other free and loyal men that the lord king's park of Ridlington and
other his demesne woods have been impaired since the last pleas of the forest
by Peter de Neville and by his foresters, bailiffs and salesmen by their gifts and
by their takings of timber for the houses of the same Peter, and by their sales
and their takings for limekilns made in the forest for the use of the same Peter,
and for supporting several hearths for making charcoal, which [sales and gifts]
were made in the bailiwick of the aforesaid Peter for the use of the same Peter
to the amount of seven thousand oaks and fuel trees and other trees and more;
the price of each oak, fuel tree and tree being twelve pence. Total, three
hundred and fifty pounds. But the injury done to the underwood and
branchwood in the aforesaid park and in the aforesaid woods by the aforesaid
Peter and his foresters, bailiffs and salemen aforesaid during the aforesaid time
cannot in any way be estimated, as it witnessed by the aforesaid persons.

From Turner's 'Select Pleas'

Figure 7.9
An eyre was a circuit around which the King's justices travelled, visiting each
shire court. They administered many different aspects of justice, especially
regarding county administration. In this extract Peter de Neville is arraigned
on a charge of abuse of his position as head forester. Conduct such as his
contributed much to the destruction and eventual disafforestation of
Royal Forests.

Ridlington. The wooded area had not seen an expansion in real terms, as certain individual woodlands had been conveniently lumped together and listed under one general name. Others had been ignored or omitted if they did not fall within the brief of the compilers of the inventory.

Speed's map of Rutland, drawn up about the year 1611 represents a commendable, if not entirely accurate effort to depict the woodlands of the early 17th century. It also emphasises the contribution of Ridlington Park to the wooded nature of the landscape.

The end of Leighfield as a Royal Forest came at about the same time as that of Leicester Forest and was determined by much the same group of factors. In 1630 Charles I removed the Royal protection and the land was sold. By the end of the century nearly all the woods had been cleared, the ancient boundaries reorganized and the land converted to pasture and tillage.

Forest of Rutland — The Parks

*L*iddington Park. Henry, bishop of Lincoln, had licence from King John (1199-1216) to enclose his park at Liddington.[35] The licence was confirmed by Henry III in 1229.[36] Fifty or so years later Edward I stocked the park with deer[37] and in 1332 it was enlarged by 60 acres and surrounded by a stone wall.[38] As late as 1611 it still contained woodland[39] but by 1650 it had been turned over to agriculture.

*R*idlington Park played a key role in the administration of the Royal Forest. It is first recorded in 1269 when the extensive wooded parts were already fenced to protect them from grazing animals and other hazards.[40] Throughout the 14th and 15th centuries the park remained an extensive and important reserve of wood; timber and wood pasture but there is no record of woodland beyond the middle of the 17th century.

*F*litteris Park was created in 1252 when Henry III granted to Richard, earl of Cornwall, the right to enclose his wood of Oakham.[41] Whether or not it was part of the Royal Forest at this time is not clear, but it extended over approximately 220 acres. Both woodland and deer co-existed until well into modern times.[42]

*C*old Overton Park, which lay wholly in Leicestershire and adjoined Flitteris Park, is first heard of in 1226-27 in a perambulation of the Forest of Rutland.[43] Much of the bank and ditch of the original pale line survive to the present, indicating an area of about 200 acres. It is doubtful whether the park existed as a deer park much beyond the close of the 15th century. Cold Overton Park Wood, an ancient woodland site, still occupies the south-east corner of the former park.

Charnwood Forest

*C*harnwood in the Middle Ages was a *chace* composed of the wastes of several surrounding manors and, as such, was always under the control of the manorial lords rather than the crown. It was poor land and offered pasture, rough grazing and a source of stone, wood and timber to the local population.[44]

Domesday Book provides only a vague notion of the landscape of central Charnwood and in particular understates the woodland which later records indicate existed in 1086. We are probably safe in the belief that the landscape of rolling hills and boggy valleys supported considerable areas of woodland. Some of this was dense and continuous; but much was open and provided pasture for small scattered groups of domestic sheep and cattle, together with the herds of wild grazers.

Charnwood was not subject to the restrictions imposed by Royal Forest status. Incursions into the waste took place more freely as the rural population began to rise in the late 11th and early 12th centuries. Land of a manor converted to agriculture with the consent of the lord was thus 'assarted'. Such assarts were usually ditched, banked and fenced thus removing them from the common grazing and bringing them under private control. Prime areas of woodland were also sometimes safeguarded in this way.

The largest settlements within the waste were the monastic houses of Grace Dieu, Alderman's Haw, Charley and Ulverscroft. With the exception of Alderman's Haw, all enclosed considerable areas including some woodlands. In addition, they ran flocks and herds on the unprotected areas where there was common grazing.

The expansion of the cultivated areas of surrounding villages ate relentlessly into the unfenced waste areas of Charnwood. The lords of Groby were particularly vigorous in promoting the exploitation of resources which would produce a profit. In 1288 Newtown Linford – the new town by the ford where the lime trees grow – is first recorded as paying rent to Lord Ferrers.[45] On the opposite side of the Forest, Woodhouse Eaves is first noticed in 1284 as a community established from Old Woodhouse, itself a daughter village of Barrow-upon-Soar.[46]

It was manorial custom to regulate the numbers of domestic grazers which individual tenants might turn out on to the waste. When populations of sheep and cattle were small, grassland turned to scrub-land and scrub-land to woodland. When populations were high, grazing became intense. Little or no regeneration of shrub and tree species took place and open grassland prevailed. With the possible exception of the years following the first outbreak of the Black Death (1348), attempts at imposing restrictions were seldom successful. Thus the nature of the landscape underwent a slow and long term change towards a more open scene where trees were few.

At the time of Domesday Book there was little if any regard for woodland conservation. A century later it was a major concern. Problems brought about by uncontrolled grazing apart, grants of wood and timber were made on such a generous basis as to indicate a reckless disregard for the long-term survival of woodland. Moreover, theft of trees was common and other forms of malpractice were rife. Thus, from the beginning of the 13th century, the first records of individual

inclosed woods, such as 'Birch Wood' appear. The creation of the hunting parks also
proved to be a major contribution to the conservation of early woodland.

Figure 7.11 indicates the locations of most of the known medieval woodlands
on Charnwood.[47] Others are more difficult to account for. The register of Leicester
Abbey, compiled towards the end of the 15th century, records Phillip Wood,
Southwood and Barrowlands in the manor of Barrow, but their locations can at

THE COLONISATION OF CHARNWOOD

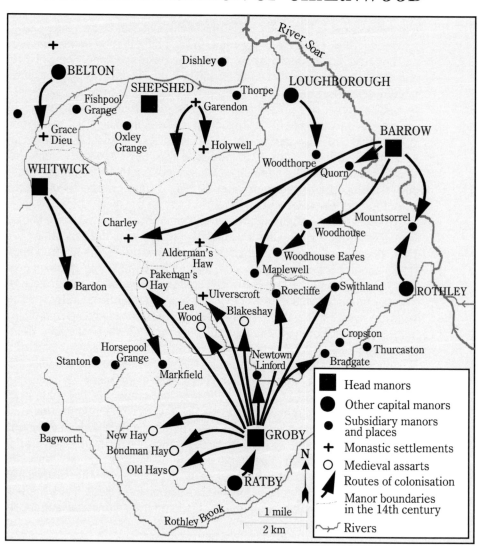

Figure 7.10
The colonisation of Charnwood Forest during the middle ages.
This diagram is based on an interpretation of numerous documentary
sources (for which see references), and offers an indication of the routes
by which the Charnwood landscape, and its tree cover, was exploited.

present only be a matter of conjecture. Several more from the same and other sources remain a complete mystery.

The total landscape of Charnwood in the mid 16th century presented two distinctly different aspects. Assarting from the waste had by this time almost ceased and large areas were inclosed and carefully managed for private profit by owners or their tenants. Virtually all the surviving woodland owed its survival to this fact. The other face of Charnwood was that created by the ever-increasing numbers of grazers competing for finite resources of pasture and heath. The cutting and removal of hundreds of ancient oaks in an advanced stage of decay marked the disappearance of the last vestiges of woodland which had been present since the late 11th century.

By the turn of the 18th century large tracts of Charnwood totalling some 12,000 acres, were in an advanced state of agricultural and ecological degeneration. 'Quite bare and naked, containing no timber nor underwood not even the remaining appearance or vestige of any' reported Pitt at the time.[48] Potter, in 1842, describes it as 'Heathery wastes' and 'rugged rock and moorland' supporting little more than flocks of 'little forest sheep'.[49] Rabbits, running free from several warrens, added to the problem. Inclosure by Act of Parliament was seen to be the solution.

The implementation of the terms of the Act of 1808 eventually transformed the ancient landscape into the framework of the one we see today.[50] Considerable areas of the newly inclosed land were planted with trees, as gentlemen competed to enhance the appearance and value of their estates. At Charnwood Lodge, Thomas Gisborne of Yoxall planted the magnificent fox covert which bears his name today. Similarly, Thomas Babington of Rothley planted large areas of Benscliffe Hill.

The two world wars took a heavy toll on Charnwood's woodlands. Between 1914 and 1950 extensive oak woodland was felled at The Outwoods, Benscliffe, Blakeshay, Lea Wood, Poultney Wood and Bardon Hill. Re-planting during the inter-war and post-war years at Blakeshay, Benscliffe and Lea Wood was almost entirely of conifers and in many cases centuries of richness and diversity of the wildlife were finally destroyed.

Charnwood Forest — the Parks[51]

Quorn Park had been established by 1135 by Ranulf, 4th earl of Chester.[52] It contained Buddon Wood which was the Domesday woodland of Barrow-upon-Soar and which survived the breakup of the park in 1273. Recent quarrying activities have almost totally destroyed the ancient sessile oak woodland and its wealth of wildlife.

Loughborough Park expanded from a modest beginning to reach westwards to include The Outwoods, the Domesday wood of the manor of Loughborough. Until well into the 17th century the park and its woodland provided an important supply of wood and timber to many local communities. Although much of the Park is now farmland and housing, the Outwoods remain as a well wooded area open to public use.

Beaumanor Park is first recorded in 1277 when the underwood was worth £6 a year.[53] In the following century much illegal hunting took place on account of the unpopularity of the frequently absent owners, the Despensers. By the end of the 16th century much of the estate's woodland and deer had vanished but many individual oaks of great size were still present in the late 19th century.

Figure 7.11 (opposite – see below for key to woodland names)
The woodlands of Charnwood Forest in the late middle ages.
The map shows approximate positions of woods known from field
work and documentary sources. See figure 7.4 for further details.

Key to the Medieval Woodlands of Charnwood Forest.

Parish/Manor	Map No. and Name	Earliest record
Belton	1. Belton Low Wood	*
Grace Dieu	2. Grace Dieu Wood	*
Shepshed	3. Kitehaw Acre	1474
	4. Little Haw	1325
Loughborough	5. Hollywell	1330
	6. Burley	*
	7. Outwoods	1343
Beaumanor	8. Mucklin	1477
	9. Beaumanor	1559
Quorn	10. Rowhele	1280
	11. Buddon	1280
Rothley	12. Rothley Plain [the lord's wood]	*
	13. Villagers Wood	*
	14. Tempilland	*
Swithland	15. Swithland Wood	*
Charley	16. Baudwin Castell	1481
	17. Birch Wood	1227
	18. Burrow Wood	*
	19. Cathill Wood	1260
	20. Timberwood	1282
Whitwick	21. Hollyhayes	1240
	22. Bardon	*
Ulverscroft/Groby	23. Lea Wood	*
	24. Blakeshay	1343
Groby	25. Lawn Wood	1331
	26. Old Wood	*
	27. Stewards Hay	1445
	28. Lady's Hay	1343
	29. Sheet Hedges	1348
	30. Martinshaw	*
Ratby	31. Ratby Burroughs	*
Thornton	32. Wood of Thornton	14th C

denotes there are no medieval references, but there is a very strong inference of a wood's existence in medieval times, from post medieval sources

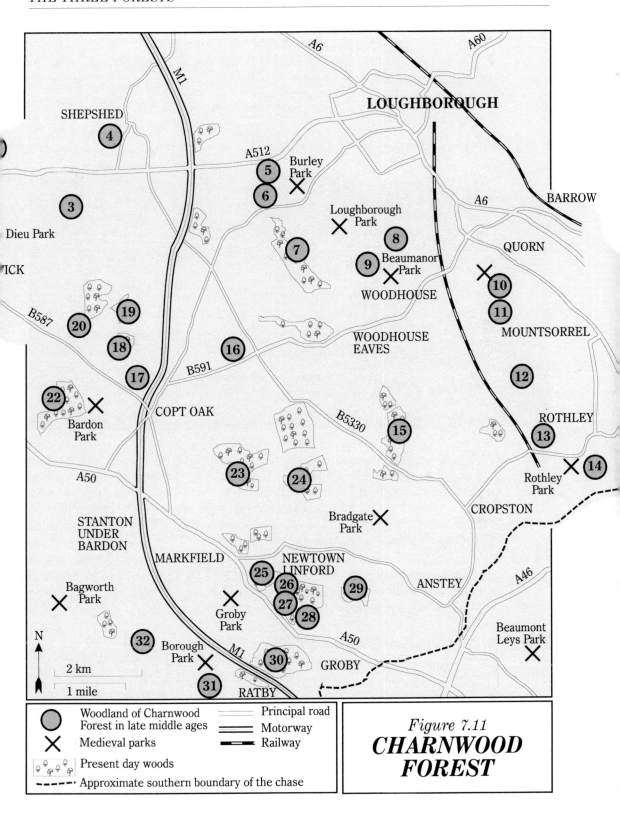

Figure 7.11
*CHARNWOOD
FOREST*

Woodland of Charnwood Forest in late middle ages
Medieval parks
Present day woods
Approximate southern boundary of the chase

Principal road
Motorway
Railway

Figure 7.12
Gisborne's Gorse, on Charnwood Lodge Nature Reserve.

B*radgate Park* began as a typical small hunting park established by the Ferrers of Groby and was greatly expanded in c.1490 by Thomas Grey, 1st marquis of Dorset. Many ancient trees were included in his park and new ones planted. Many fine old oaks have survived here to the present carrying with them irreplaceable physical, ecological and historical associations with the past. The Park contains a number of more recent spinneys, and is open to the public.

A few ancient oaks still survive in tiny spinneys at ***Groby***, where they mark the site of another Ferrers park first recorded in 1279.[54] Sales of wood and hay indicate the familiar divisions into compartments. In 1512 woodland products from the park were worth 73s and the grazing in Martinshaw Wood, which adjoined the park, was worth 5s.[54]

B*ardon Park,* containing c.1260 acres, originally occupied the whole of Bardon Hill. However, by 1427 it had contracted to a small area around the summit, a victim of the social and economic changes following the outbreak of the Black Death in the previous century.[55] It was at one time an important site for mosses and liverworts until large areas were felled and planted with conifers. A small area of interesting wood, on the southern flank of the hill, is all that survives today.

B*orough Park* at Ratby was created later in the 13th century and later enlarged by Anthony Bek, bishop of Durham.[57] It enclosed and incorporated woodland known then, as now, as Ratby Burroughs.

*B*urleigh Park was a late creation and is first heard of in 1330 and included Burleigh Wood.[58] The park adjoined Holywell Wood which has a long documentary history as an ancient woodland. In 1468/9 wood from both Holywell and Burleigh together was worth £20.[59] Ninety years later it was worth only 20s.[60] Much of the site is now covered by houses and the giant British Gas complex.

*A*t *Shepshed* the park was associated with, but did not include, the two ancient sites of Oakley and Piper Woods. It is first recorded in 1230[61] and had ceased to exist after 1480.[62] Although both woods survive, the site of the park is now under the M1 Motorway.

*T*he Parks of *Belton* and *Grace Dieu* were both associated with the nunnery of Grace Dieu. Belton Park disappeared at a very early date. The latter, which adjoined Grace Dieu Wood, disappeared with the nunnery at the Dissolution in the 1530s.

Figure 7.13
Bradgate Park from the air.

Chapter Eight
Woodland from 1530 to 1720

*T*he Dissolution of the Monasteries by Henry VIII heralded a period of great social, political and economic change in England. In 1530 the quantity of woodland and its distribution in Leicestershire and Rutland was very much as it had been 300 years earlier. This was, as the traveller John Leland had observed:– 'Such part of Leicestershire as is lying by south and east [is] in champain [open fields] and hath little wood. And such part of Leicestershire as lyeth by west and north has much wood'.[1] Change on the county's landscape was primarily a result of the growth of the human population which, by 1600, had regained its level of 1377.[2] During the following one hundred years the increase was somewhat slower and uneven, as different parts of the county felt the effects of inclosure. The 17th century also saw the emergence of industry, notably the hosiery trade, which was to transform the county a century and a half later.

The downfall of the monasteries was organised by teams of commissioners who sought out and catalogued the assets and holdings, including the woodland, of each House. With the exception of those for Leicester Abbey, few pre-inquisition records have survived and the edited version of the commissioners' returns lacks important detail. Thus it is not possible to construct a map to show the whereabouts of the ancient monastic woodlands. However, it is clear that of the 62 Houses with land in Leicestershire only about a dozen held anything more than the odd small estate. Of these Garendon and Ulverscroft together held about 1400 acres of woodland which accounts for between 50% and 60% of the woodland for which records survive or for which inferences can be made. Only four other houses:– Owston, Langley, Dalby and Leicester Abbey had 100 acres of woodland or more.[3]

The release of monastic land, much of it locked up in the mortmain (dead hand) of the church for centuries, stimulated a strong land market which was to flourish up to and beyond the Civil War (1642–45). After a brisk start the new secular landlords emerged as men of mostly local families such as the Greys, the Hastings and the Manners. Thomas Grey for example bought the site of Langley Priory with its woodland. (see figure 8.1)[4] The religious houses had been major holders of Leicestershire woodlands and his purchase reflected the fact that, by and large, they had managed their woods well. It is perhaps surprising to discover there is little or no evidence to suggest that the new owners exploited their new woodlands for the sake of a quick return, i.e. in modern terms, fell to asset-stripping.[5] The beginning of Elizabeth's reign saw the quantity and distribution of woodland in Leicestershire changed very little over the two previous important decades.

Also unchanged in Leicestershire was the landscape of small, scattered nucleated villages with their large open fields and scattered heaths, a pattern also characteristic of other parts of Midland England. To the world of small farmers came the improvers, such as Fitzherbert and Tusser, whose interests in agricultural advancement brought change in the form of inclosure. Between 1540 and 1607 some

Figure 8.1

Thomas Gray's Purchase of Langley Priory 1543[4]
(Part)

The demesne of the late Priory of Langley

The Park Wood containeth	20 acres
The Short Wood "	6 acres
The Owk [sic] Wood "	30 acres
The Horse Coppy "	15 acres
The Park Spring "	20 acres

In Calver Close be 2 acres
Hedgerows about the demesne contain an acre

Whereof is waste [common] 8 acres, 4 acres destroyed with cattle, 13 acres of 10 years growth and 3 acres of 11 years growth... there for his [Gray's] housebote, hedgebote, fire bote, ploughbote and cartbote which he hath yearly... therefore not valued 3 acres of 10 years growth (£15), 20 acres of 22 years growth (£40), 3 acres of 15 years growth (100 shillings), 30 acres of 1 year's growth (£30), 10 acres thin set of 30 years growth (65 shillings and 8d).

The Spring of the wood or ground of 30 acres aforesaid not valued because they lie open and common and hath not been used to be inclosed and 16 acres not valued because they be residue, and 48 acres residue not valued because the herbage is demised for a yearly rent charged of the valuation of the lands.

Trees growing about the situations of the said tenants and in hedges inclosing lands pertaining to the same will barely suffice for timber to repair the said tenants and to maintain the hedges and fences about the same therefore [they have not been] valued.

75 villages saw the first appearance of hedged fields but, of these, at most 19 were entirely inclosed. By 1607 at least a quarter of Leicestershire was inclosed. One and a half generations later one in three Leicestershire villages was entirely inclosed as the movement quickened in pace. The pattern was already an untidy one, owing more to soil and climate than to land ownership. Inclosure by agreement was becoming the means by which improving landlords sought to increase their incomes. The 13 inclosures which took place during the interregnum all resulted in the inclosure of entire villages. During the fifty years following 1660, 41 places were entirely inclosed so that by 1710 47% of the area of the county lacked land worked

in common. The new inclosures, of course, meant hedges and these were most suitable places for growing trees for timber and firewood.[6]

The crown had retained some monastic woodland for its own use but subsequent management of this in Leicestershire was to prove to be no better than in the woodlands it had anciently held. The survey in 1608 of Leicestershire Crown Woods and Forests showed that in Leicester Forest, where neglect and abuse were greatest, only 4,225 timber oaks and 'decayed fuel oaks' together worth about £900 survived. In the Royal Parks around Leicester Forest the situation was somewhat better, with 60% of the 8,000 trees present valued at 8s each. Moreover, the coppice in Tooley Park was worth 18s 8d an acre. The situation in Rutland was altogether much better. Leighfield Forest contained 9,000 trees, three quarters of which were timber trees and valued at 10s each. Also, as regards their timber, Rutland parks were much better managed, although the 1,800 recorded acres of coppice were worth only about 1s-4d per acre on average.[7]

Scattered over the county were certain isolated woods which were still in the hands of the crown. The largest of these was Launde (Big or West) Wood, formerly part of a large medieval park, where the 2,236 oaks were valued at £1,500.[8] Hinckley Wood, also part of a former deer park, covered 70 acres which supported 4,200 trees and had underwood worth 5s 8d an acre. The wood, it was claimed, supplied the needs of the Duchy of Lancaster's tenants in the neighbourhood and in Leicester.[9] It was also realized that the poor state of the reserves was giving cause for concern

for the future. Elsewhere in Leicestershire there were various small woods, mostly former monastic properties in the hands of the crown, such as those at Packington (5 acres), Ingarsby (6 acres) Woodhouse (6 acres), and the four at Hallaton:– Dryhill (8 acres), Blood Wood (30 acres), Horse Wood (60 acres) and Small Wood (10 acres).[10]

Timber in the hedges and closes of crown lands away from the parks and Forests reflected a similar dismal record of neglect. The closes surveyed in 1608 were mostly those of the former lands of Henry Grey of Bradgate, duke of Suffolk, executed in 1554.[11] The nine and a half thousand trees on the uninclosed parts of Charnwood Forest were worth only 1 shilling each. 'Great waste hath been committed' the surveyors reported, 'by whom we know not'. Some of these decaying trees or doddards' [old decaying trees] were however worth saving from the axe 'because they will bear good tops in time to make yearly sale'. The two thousand five hundred trees in Ratby Cow Pasture were also considered as worth sparing 'because they all die at the tops having been cut off in the midst'. Hedgerow trees were usually marked so that tenants could

Figure 8.2
An ancient oak at Groby.
Several such trees survive in tiny spinneys, and are the last survivors of the ancient hunting park.

repair their houses, but in most cases the reserves listed in the survey were considered inadequate for future needs.

Much of the remaining non-royal woodland was growing in the parks of nobility and gentry. Some of these parks were descended in part from earlier deer inclosures. Others were newly constructed for the purpose of ornamenting the great houses of the Elizabethan years. Some parks supported deer but all contained woodland, some of it old and well established as at Market Bosworth, Croxton Kerrial and Castle Donington. Post medieval creations such as Newhall, Nevill Holt and Exton were also set out with woodland with a view to producing the fashionable landscape of the time. Garendon, also a post medieval creation, carried a truly colossal quantity of timber.[12]

An important source of information for the period 1500–1650 is the numerous documents known as *fines* which record details of dealings and agreements of various descriptions regarding land transactions which did not involve the crown. Those available for Leicestershire give a good coverage of the county and provide a clear idea of the presence or absence of woodland.[13] Taken as a whole they reveal nothing new in principle about woodland and simply confirm the pattern which was, by the year 1600, centuries old.

Figure 8.3

A Breviat of the Survey of His Majesty's Woods and Timber 1608[11]								
	Timber			'Other Small Trees'			Decaying trees		
Parish	No.	£ Val.	Av. Val.	No.	£ Val.	Av Val.	No.	£ Val.	Av. Val.
Kilworth Kibworth Beauchamp	51	11	4.3s	431	578	26.82s	0	-	-
Smeaton	23	2	1.74s	40	3	1.5s	0	-	-
Ratby	0	-	-	2584	145.3s	1.12s	2000	150	1.5s
Botcheston	0	-	-	1246	79	1.26s	0	-	-
Whitwick	175	26	2.97s	0	-	-	6289	314.9s	0.1s
Charnwood Forest	163	16	1.96s	9570	487.10s	1s	0	-	-
Hugglescote	37	3.14s	0.2s	0	-	-	376	16.19s	0.9s
Donington	21	2	1.90s	0	-	-	209	9.8s	0.89s
Newtown Linford	86	6	1.39s	200	8.6s	0.11d	0	-	-
Kegworth	200	3	0.3s	186	17.3.8d	1.83s	0	-	-
Markfield	500	50	0.2s	1952	67.12s	0.68s	509	30	1.17s
Bardon Park	23	24	3.90s	0	-	-	2102	160	1.52s

Figure 8.4

LEICESTERSHIRE CROWN WOODS AND FORESTS – 1608								
Timber Trees			Decaying Trees			Coppice (C) and Small Beeches (B)		
No.	Val. £	Av.	No.	Val. £	Av.	Acres	Val. £	Av.
EXCHEQUER								
Leicester Forest	163	16	2s	9570	478 .10s	1s	0	-	-
Leicester Parks	2753	1524	11s	2102	160	1s6d	0	-	-
Leighfield Forest	6955	3610 .14s	10s2½d	2326	826 .5s	7s1d	1152 (C)	96.19s 1½d	1s8d
Rutland Parks	3361	1962 .11s	11s8d	1017	335 .4s	6s6d	967 (C)	33.13s 4d	1s
DUCHY OF LANCASTER								
Leicester Forest	3055	667 .1s	4s4d	117	214 .7s4d	3s7d	0	-	-
Tooley Park	2102	494	4s8d	1086	204 .1s	3s9d	270 (B)	252.12 s4d	18s7d

The Civil War brought about widespread social and economic disruption in many parts of England. Local conflict in Leicestershire centred on the rivalry between the Grey family on the side of parliament and the Hastings family for the crown. There are few records on the effect of the war on woodland, although many local people must have made the most of the uncertain times to exploit their local resources. Of the royalists, William Cavendish (who was abroad for most of the war) returned home to find that in his park at Clipsham 'not one timber tree was left'.[14] In Leicestershire, Ferdinando Hastings sold Buddon Wood for £2,100 in 1654 in order to help meet the demands of the parliamentary sequestrators.[15]

Considerable expansion of the Leicestershire coal industry took place during the reign of Elizabeth (1558-1603). The reliance on coal in the economy of north-west Leicestershire and south Derbyshire was well established. Although poor communications proved a major handicap to distribution, the rising local demand meant that the two main entrepreneurs, the Beaumonts and the Willoughbys, could sell all they could mine. Production was probably brought to a halt by the Civil War but resumed and expanded in the late 17th century, when charcoal for iron smelting added to the demand for timber.[16]

This increase in coal and iron production placed new demands on local woodlands. Timbers removed from excavations of 15th century mines at Coleorton show the use of oak and field maple as timbers for lining shafts and supporting the roofs of the galleries. Woodland in local parks met the bulk of the demand. Bosworth Park, well wooded since Doomesday, was still a major source[17] as was Seal Wood (then in Leicestershire but now in Derbyshire). In the late 16th century, Henry Beaumont re-established Coleorton Park, on what was then the site of abandoned mines. It was planted with trees and stocked with deer.[18] Away from the park and other ancient woodland sites, coalmining produced an ever-changing landscape. This situation contrasted very strongly with the general situation in the rest of the county.

Figure 8.5
An oak pit prop used
by 15th century
coalminers.
It was unearthed at
Coleorton during
modern open-cast
mining.

Chapter Nine

Woodland from 1720 to 1914

*T*he years 1720-1914 saw enormous social and economic changes in Great Britain. The major advances in agriculture of the eighteenth century, together with the arrival of the Industrial Revolution in the following one, gave rise to an explosion in the numbers of the human population. In 1801 Leicester contained about 17,000 people. Two generations later there were 60,000 inhabitants and by the year 1901 about 211,000, indicating a thirteen fold increase during the nineteenth century. The major towns of the county also grew rapidly as manufacturing centres, and burst out into the surrounding countryside. Networks of canals, railways and modern roads were established to move raw materials, goods and the products of the extractive industries. As the Empire expanded, trade and commerce developed a world-wide dimension. Many aspects of these two centuries of change were reflected directly or indirectly on our local landscape. This chapter looks at some of the more interesting of these as they affected the woodland.

The Parliamentary Acts of the eighteenth and early nineteenth centuries brought to a close a long history of inclosure in the two counties and transformed the open field landscape, by then a thousand years old, to the familiar patchwork pattern we know today. Increases in the price of food (especially the rising price of corn); the easily reached markets of the growing industrial centres; the technical advances which allowed difficult terrain to be tackled and the lack of organised opposition in many places combined to form an unstoppable movement for inclosure. In Leicestershire between 1720 and 1849, one hundred and fifty-six Acts enclosed approximately 237,000 acres or 45 per cent of the county, (see figure 9.1). In Rutland, thirty Acts enclosed approximately 41,000 acres which represented about 47 per cent of the total area.

A major consequence of the Inclosures was the disappearance of the remaining heathlands of Leicestershire. These included Croxton Kerrial (1766), Saltby (1771), Bagworth (1794), Ashby Woulds (1800), Great Easton (1804) and Newbold Verdon (1810). The inclosure of the 12,000 acres of Charnwood Forest, the largest heath of all, together with Rothley Plain, was accounted for by the single Act of 1808. The heathlands were the areas of the poorest soils and were most unattractive for agriculture. However, freed from the chaotic management of the last vestiges of the manorial system, they were drained, deep-ploughed and limed and transformed in both production and appearance.

The Inclosures had little or no affect on the pattern of ancient woodland. Elsewhere, the former uncontrolled grazing by domestic stock on common land was removed and woodland regeneration became possible once again. The terms of the Acts created a huge demand for posts and rails which protected the young hawthorn hedges in their early years. At the same time, the creation of many additional field boundaries encouraged the planting of trees in hedgerows, the rich legacy of which was enjoyed to the early 1950s.

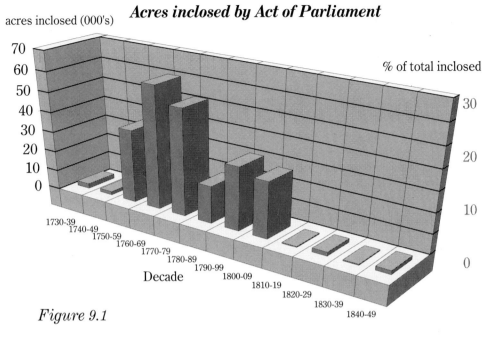

INCLOSURES IN LEICESTERSHIRE 1730-1849
Acres inclosed by Act of Parliament

acres inclosed (000's)

% of total inclosed

Figure 9.1

But perhaps the greatest single impact of the Inclosures with regard to the woodland was the stimulus which was provided for new plantings. Scattered holdings were often translated into compact blocks of land which could be administered more easily. Often, smallholders found themselves unable to make a living and were obliged to sell their allotments. Throughout the eighteenth and nineteenth centuries the large estates tended to grow larger in size. By 1883 four families owned one quarter of Rutland and the duke of Rutland owned 30,000 acres in the north-east of Leicestershire, (see figure 9.2).[1]

Gentlemen planted to improve the appearance of their property, to invest for income and to make provision for sporting purposes. Around Belvoir Castle the duke of Rutland had 'pleasure grounds, woods and plantations' extending over 500 acres, with a total woodland area of 1700 acres.[2] Lord Berners built Keythorpe Hall in 1843, the grounds of which were 'tastefully laid out and terminated with extensive plantations'.[3] Sir George Beaumont of Coleorton sought to hide the scars of coal mining by planting the numerous clay and slack banks which had been thrown up in various parts of the parish.[4] Lord Ferrers planted at Ragdale, the earl of Moira at Castle Donington and the Heathcotes at Normanton.

The most extensive planting took place on the wild and rocky acres of Charnwood Forest where the Greys owned much of the land. Planting was not confined to the traditional woodland species. At Benscliffe, Scots pine, spruce and 'firs' were often included with the oak and other hardwood species. (See figure 9.5).[5] Planting for timber production was modified to accommodate the strong sporting interests of successive earls of Stamford. The sporting estate centred on Bradgate Park, where the numerous spinneys in the 'High Park' were established by the sixth earl in order to promote pheasant shooting.

At Langton the Reverend William Hanbury, the vicar and a man of private means, developed his interest in growing trees with a view to raising an income for local needy people. In 1751 he obtained seeds locally and from abroad, particularly North America, and began the development of extensive nurseries. Two years later he had 20,000 young trees. In 1757 large plantations in the parish of Gumley were made which, within a year, were valued at £10.000. Seven years on the trees were sold to provide a profit. Although Hanbury published the details of his scheme, which received widespread acclaim, his enterprises came to an end with his death.[6]

The traditional open field landscape of Leicestershire and Rutland had been a great encouragement to the rise of foxhunting. Although inclosures brought barriers to long, unbroken runs they also brought opportunities for encouraging foxes. Small

Figure 9.2

The Great Landowners of Leicestershire and Rutland 1883[1]		
(Figures in acres. Family names in brackets)		
	Leicestershire	Rutland
1. Duke of Rutland (Manners)	30,188	764
2. Earl of Gainsborough (Noel)	–	15,076
3. Lord Aveland (Heathcote)	–	13,633
4. Earl of Loudon (Hastings)	10,174	–
5. Earl Howe (Curzon)	9,755	–
6. Marquis of Exeter (Cecil)	553	8,998
7. George Henry Finch	–	9,183
8. Earl of Stamford & Warrington (Grey)	9,012	–
9. Earl of Dysart (Tollemache)	8,420	22
10. Mrs. Perry Herrick	6,560	–
11. Harry Powys-Keck	6,529	–
12. Harry Tyrwhitt-Wilson	5,768	2
13. Edward Hartopp	5,423	–
14. Sir Alexander Dixie, Bt.	5,379	–
15. Nathaniel Curzon	4,753	–
16. Earl of Lovelace (Milbanke)	4,568	–
17. Major Clagett and the Countess of Harborough	4,521	5
18. Lord Brooke (Greville)	4,411	–
19. Earl of Aylesford (Finch)	4,272	–
20. Edward Frewen	4,218	55

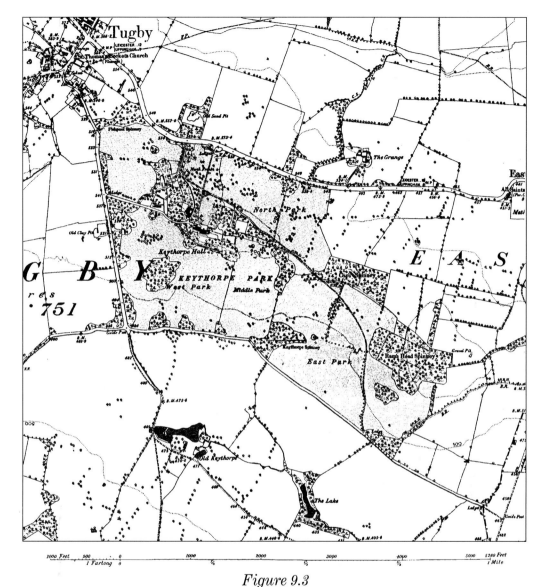

Figure 9.3
Keythorpe Hall and Park in 1884, as shown in the first series Ordnance Survey
map. This was the landscape created in Victorian times by Lord Berners

woods, variously known under the name of *'covert'*, *'gorse'*, *'furze'* and *'thorns'*, and typically five to ten acres in size, appeared on the landscape. Some were the result of natural regeneration, where land had been fenced from domestic grazers. Others were deliberate creations and were planted with ash and oak. In all these woods it was considered important to develop a thick ground cover and low shrub layer where foxes could find shelter as well as hunt. Such woods were usually integrated into the pattern of existing woods so that foxes were always available over a wide

*Figure 9.4
Belvoir Castle
and Woods.
The woodland here
was planted in a
conscious attempt
to enhance the
appearance of the
landscape in the
vicinity of the
Duke of Rutland's
residence.*

area. Thus were established the conditions leading to a 'good day's run' for which the countryside of Leicestershire and Rutland became so widely known.

Although the post-Inclosure plantings had a considerable effect on the appearance of some areas of the two counties, the increase in the total amount of woodland was small. Moreover, it was in the undisturbed ancient parks that the very old trees and the ancient avenues were to be found. In most cases these areas escaped the attention of the landscape gardeners, although Humphry Repton worked at Castle Donington (1790), at Buckminster (1791) and at Burley (1795); and Uvedale Price landscaped Coleorton (1810). Beaumanor, Bradgate, Donington,

Figure 9.5

Tree Planting on Charnwood Forest By The Greys of Groby[5]

1820 - On Hogsback in Charnwood Forest		1821	
		Sharpley Hill	13,500
		Groby Parks	2,025
Oak	14,470	Newtown Linford Lane	10,780
Beech	6,850		
Holly	860	TOTAL =	26,305
Ash	12,500		
Spruce	6,130	1822	
Mountain Ash	600	Groby Parks	
Larch	12,330	Sharpley Hill }	3,900
Birch	4,304	Crow Hill	
Poplar	970	Markfield Gate	750
'Scotch Fir'	9,240	Rothley Plain	750
		Hollgate Hill	31,425
TOTAL =	68,254	TOTAL =	36,825
		GRAND TOTAL =	115,859

Figure 9.6

Charges of ffalling, Cutting, Sawing, Carrying and Ranking Staunton [Harold] 1726[10]

April

Paid for felling 6 acres, 1 rood, 39 perches in Springwood to Tunnicliffe and partners	£1.18s0d
Paid them for felling ash poles in Springwood	3s0d
Paid for turning out 300 of stoops and railes	15s0d
Paid for turning out 800 of winding hazels	8s0d
Paid for 10 hundred of Great Poles at 2s 6d per 100	£1.5s0d
Paid for cropping 194 trees at 1$\frac{1}{2}$d and 10 days falling Barks to Tunicliffe	£1.14s3d
Paid for 164 cord of colewood cutting at 18s per cord	£12.6s
Paid for 164 cord ranking at 4d per100 cord	£2.14s8d

May

Paid John Richards, John and George his sons 34 days at $\frac{1}{2}$d cropping and dressing up the holes of the trees in the Park that was broken down by the wind and snow	£1.14s6d

July

Paid Richards cutting [wood] up 20 days and $\frac{1}{2}$	£1.0s6d
Paid for ranking 69 cord and 2 foot in the Park at 14d per 100 cord	£1.3s
Paid Geo. Ratchet and partner 1 days cross cutting in the Park	2s
Paid for falling 2 great Runneling trees in the Park 10$\frac{1}{2}$ days	10s-6
Paid 3 Grover's 29 days and $\frac{1}{2}$ carrying poles and heaping thorns in Spring Wood	19s-08
Paid woodcutters for cutting and ranking 255 cord of colewood at 22s per cord	£25.07s6d
Paid for kidding in the Lountwood	5s

from the wood book of lord Ferrers, 1726

Staunton Harold, Market Bosworth, Croxton Kerrial and Exton contained ancient trees with their associated flora and fauna. In some places late seventeenth century and early eighteenth century emparking, such as that at Stapleford, Normanton, Wistow and Misterton, also added to the wooded landscape. In 1867 the writer Shirley noted that the two counties contained ten deer parks which extended over a total of five-and-a-half thousand acres and contained almost 3,000 deer.[7]

If owners of land were planting for their own interests, the situation did not please successive governments. Between 1786 and 1807 the price of coppice wood doubled, that of timber trebled and the price paid for ash bark for the tanning industry quadrupled. It was the shortage of oak for the navy that caused the greatest concern. In 1792 it was noted that in both hedges and woods the supply had decreased in Leicestershire. In Rutland the situation was little better.[8] Writing in 1809, Pitt made the same observations. He reluctantly concluded that, with

*Figure 9.7
Burley Wood,
Rutland, from the
south-east.*

regard to wood for domestic consumption, both counties were too fertile to support more woodland when supplies from elsewhere were available.[9]

Most productive woodlands were managed under the system of coppice-with-standards. The various tasks involved are well exemplified by the details from the wood book of lord Ferrers, shown in figure 9.6. Felling was usually a spring or summer job. The products of the coppice were *'ranked'* (organised) according to their uses. *'Stoops'* were posts to which *'rails'*, the horizontal bars, were attached to make fences. *'Colewood'* was destined for use in the coal mines and was usually sold, as was the coal itself, by the variable unit known as the *'cord'*. Very small branches and twigs, which today might be used by gardeners as pea sticks, were *'kidded'* (collected up and bound) into *'kids'* (faggots), for use mainly as fuel. Standard trees, after felling, had their trunks 'runnelled' (marked) ready for sale.[10] Up to the mid nineteenth century oak bark was carefully stripped and sold separately.

Sales were conducted in one of two ways. At Southwood, Lord Moira cut and processed the wood and timber and sold it at frequent and regular intervals to interested persons, mostly tenants for their own consumption.[11] However, it was more usual to make ready and advertise an annual sale by auction. On the Stamford estates in north-west Leicestershire the one thousand or so acres of coppice were cut in rotation every nineteen years to 1786, rising to every twenty-one years from 1816. Income from woodland fluctuated from year to year according to demand, the availability of the produce and the need of the estate for a cash injection. In 1756 wood produced £1000 per annum compared with £2656 for cottage and farm rents for that year. Between 1883 and 1919 woodlands produced fifteen per cent of the estate income.[12]

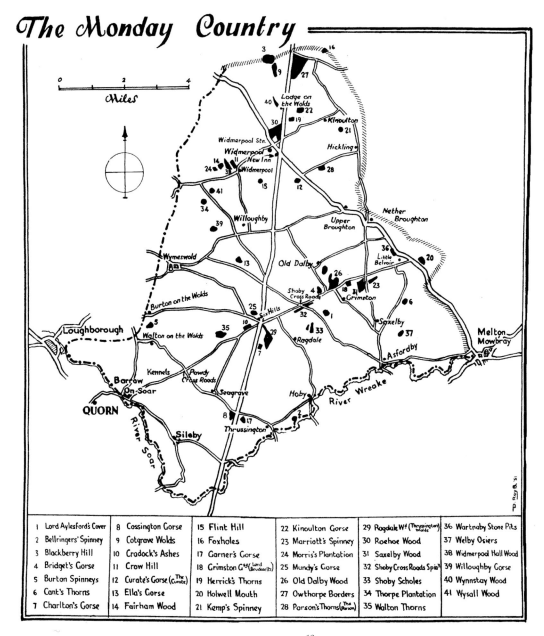

1	Lord Aylesford's Cover	8	Cossington Gorse	15	Flint Hill
2	Bellringers' Spinney	9	Cotgrave Wolds	16	Foxholes
3	Blackberry Hill	10	Cradock's Ashes	17	Garner's Gorse
4	Bridget's Gorse	11	Crow Hill	18	Grimston G.ᵐˢ (Lord Bredusells)
5	Burton Spinneys	12	Curate's Gorse (The Curate)	19	Herrick's Thorns
6	Cant's Thorns	13	Ella's Gorse	20	Holwell Mouth
7	Charlton's Gorse	14	Fairham Wood	21	Kemp's Spinney

22	Kinoulton Gorse	29	Ragdale Wᵈ (Thrussington Wolds)	36	Wartnaby Stone Pits
23	Marriott's Spinney	30	Roehoe Wood	37	Welby Osiers
24	Morris's Plantation	31	Saxelby Wood	38	Widmerpool Hall Wood
25	Mundy's Gorse	32	Shoby Cross Roads Spinⁿᵉ	39	Willoughby Gorse
26	Old Dalby Wood	33	Shoby Scholes	40	Wynnstay Wood
27	Owthorpe Borders	34	Thorpe Plantation	41	Wysall Wood
28	Parson's Thorns (The Parson)	35	Walton Thorns		

Figure 9.8[12]

The Monday Country, that area of Leicestershire and South Nottinghamshire hunted by the Quorn Hunt on Mondays. This map shows well the creation, in the 18th and 19th centuries, of many small woods, recognised by the names 'Cover', 'Thorns', 'Ashes' and 'Plantation', to provide cover for foxes. Such woods augmented the existing woodland sites, such as Old Dalby Wood, to ensure a plentiful and widespread fox population.

Improvement in communications by canal and later by railway saw the enormous development of the coal industry in Leicestershire. Mining at significantly deeper levels began in Leicestershire in the 1820s following advances in mine-technology. By 1867 annual production had risen to over one million tons.[13] Existing mines were deepened and additional ones sunk in new areas. The demand for timber for pit props had never been greater, but the inadequacies of local supplies meant that imports on a large scale from other parts of Great Britain had to be made. The increased availability of coal further reduced the use of wood as a regular source of fuel for heating and cooking in Leicestershire homes, particularly in the north-west, where pit-head prices were lower.

Towards the end of the nineteenth century it became even more obvious that the nation's supply of wood and timber was totally inadequate to meet an unexpected, sudden and heavy demand. Although various initiatives to tackle the problem were introduced at national level, when war came in 1914 many of our local woods bore their share of the catastrophe which followed.

Chapter Ten

Woodland 1914 to the Present Day

*T*he massive loss of the nation's merchant shipping in the early years of the Great War produced a sudden realization of the need for vigorous action to maximise local supplies of timber. As a result there began the felling of large areas of woodland, all done under licence to control prices and conserve supplies. In Leicestershire Holywell Wood, Blakeshay Wood, Pasture Wood, part of Launde Big Wood and others were lost during the war efforts. By 1945, with losses from World War II as well, 450,000 acres of British woodland had been removed.[1]

The lessons learnt from the early stages of the first war stimulated the production of a review of Britain's forests and the formulation of a plan of action for the future. From the Acland Report arose the Forestry Commission in 1919, the activities of which dominated forestry policy during the inter-war years and beyond. Where previously most Leicestershire and Rutland woods had been broad leaf and had been managed mainly for pheasants rather than timber, the new practice was to make plantings of conifers which were deemed more commercially viable. There was also a move in many parts of the country to acquire new areas of land, especially rough grazing, and to plant them with trees for the first time. What had previously been a haphazard, unplanned situation was replaced by Central Planning and control of resources, with grants to owners, powers to purchase land, and moves towards professional training.

This new sense of direction was accompanied by great social change among those who owned many of the counties' major woodlands. Changes in the distribution of wealth, punitive death duties and the wartime loss of male heirs saw a massive shift in political power from the landowning classes to other hands. Huge family holdings were broken up and sold to tenants and public institutions. Country houses were pulled down and the link between inherited land and wealth disappeared for good. In particular, the estate system which accounted for the existence of most of Leicestershire and Rutland's major woods did not survive the inter-war years. Between 1917 and 1921 one quarter of the land of England changed hands as between six and eight million acres were sold.

The Forestry Commission aimed to bring to an end the feeling of uncertainty about the future of home-grown timber and the chaotic state of marketing. Since most of the woodlands had been much neglected new moves towards encouraging an interest in their improvement were made. The Commission acquired no land in Leicestershire and very little in Rutland. The success of private forestry was seen to rest with the new owners of the woodlands concerned. However, when war broke out again in 1939, the oldest of the new plantings in the two counties were barely twenty years old and the prospects for the supply of timber for another major war were not encouraging.

This view proved well founded. Immediate controls over the felling, price and the use of timber were introduced, as the calamitous loss of shipping from U-boat

Figure 10.1
Coleorton 1989. Modern open cast mining techniques allow large scale
extraction of the remainder of the seams earlier miners failed to exploit fully.

action came about once again. Forestry policy was one of total exploitation with no thought for conservation, least of all nature conservation. By the summer of 1942, 1800 acres of British woodlands were being felled each week, much of it for use in the coalmines.[2] Although by no means all, many of Leicestershire's major woodlands were clear felled or almost so. Amongst those affected were Buddon Wood, Martinshaw, Blakeshay, Cloud Wood, Spring Wood, Launde Park Wood, and Owston, as were Stoke Dry Wood and Wardley Wood in Rutland. In many cases the felling effectively brought to an end many centuries of unbroken continuity of woodland cover, and resulted in a major upheaval to the wildlife communities of the ancient sites. Worst hit were those invertebrates which rely on old trees.

Even before the close of World War II provisions (which became operative in 1945) were made at national level to renew the plans for the building up of a strategic reserve of timber. A Forestry Authority would have powers to purchase three million acres of open land, most of it of low agricultural value. In addition the two million acres of existing woodland were to be systematically managed and developed. Owners of private woodland were to be offered financial and technical assistance under the 'dedication' scheme if they would manage their woods in prescribed ways and to agreed ends. The main aim in all cases was the production of a sound timber reserve which would expand to meet future needs on a local and national basis.

Figure 10.2

WOODLAND IN LEICESTERSHIRE AND RUTLAND
1947-49

(Source: Census of Woodlands 1947-49, Forestry Commission)

	Leicestershire	Rutland
Total land areas (acres)	530,248	97,087
Woodland in private hands (acres)	12,280	3,130
Woodland in state hands (acres)	-	200
Total woodland	12,280	3,330
% of total land area	2.3	3.4
% which is unproductive woodland	44	26
Area of coniferous High Forest (acres)	790	236
Area of mainly broadleaf High Forest (acres)	5,316	2,101
Area of Coppice (including coppice with standards)		
in private hands (acres)	835	130
in state hands (acres)	-	-
% of total woodland	7	4
Scrub Woodland		
in private hands (acres)	2,281	474
in state hands (acres)	-	-
% of total woodland	19	14
Devastated forest		
in private hands (acres)	762	141
in state hands (acres)	-	-
% of total woodland	6	4
Area felled since Sept. 1939		
private (acres)	2,201	228
state (acres)	-	-
% of total woodland	18	7

A survey of British Woodlands carried out between 1947 and 1949 (see above) showed that, as a proportion of total land area, only three other counties had less wood than Leicestershire and only eight had less than Rutland. It also revealed that only a little over half our local woodland was productive in the ways approved by the Forestry Authority. In Leicestershire almost one fifth of the woodland was still in a clear-felled state and was regenerating in an unordered way. Another fifth was *scrub*, inferior growth which was unlikely to develop into a saleable crop of poles or timber. Further, one in twenty acres was described as 'devastated', a condition where stands of the best timber had been removed to leave scattered or patchy remnants of the original crop which was not capable of satisfactory development. In Rutland, the situation was similar if not so acute.

The initiative towards a national forestry policy was thought to help the whole process of post-war rural planning. This included the setting up of the Nature Conservancy. It was given powers, under the 1949 National Parks and Access to the Countryside Act, to establish and manage National Nature Reserves (NNRs) and Sites of Special Scientific Interest (SSSIs). In Leicestershire and Rutland were established 23 SSSIs, of which 10 were wholly of woodland interest and 5 more partly so.

When hostilities in Europe ceased in 1945 the war against one species, the rabbit, was moving to its climax. Rabbits were once uncommon animals and confined to commercial management in purpose-built enclosures called warrens. But, taking advantage of eighteenth and nineteenth century changes in land management - nowhere more pronounced than in Leicestershire and Rutland - they had become pests and posed a serious threat to woodland trees and farmland crops alike. By 1950 rabbits out-numbered the human population and their close and incessant grazing was effectively preventing the regeneration and recovery of all but the most carefully protected woodlands. In 1953 myxomatosis broke out and reduced rabbit numbers by more than ninety-five per cent. Changes in the countryside were seen, in places little short of amazing. At Prior's Coppice a deeper sward developed on the grassy rides, with the consequent loss of several plant species which do not thrive in long grass.

A nation still short of timber ten years after the end of the war looked with interest at the supplies on farms, in hedgerows, in parks and in small spinneys. They had been subject to little planning control yet they contained valuable, if limited reserves. Many of the hedgerows of Leicestershire – 'Leafy Leicestershire' as it was known – were the creation of the Parliamentary Inclosure Movement described in chapter nine, and were particularly well treed. Further, these hedgerows were now being threatened by the early signs of what was to develop into the agri-business of the 1970s. Informed opinion maintained there was a balance to be struck between the disadvantages of trees in hedgerows and their use to the farmer. There was widespread agreement in Leicestershire and Rutland that trees were an integral part of a hedgerow, not only on account of the wildlife they harboured but also from the amenity and historic aspects. Their indirect contribution to the tourist industry, along with other things 'typically English', was thought to be considerable. Conservation and replacement were therefore important factors.[3]

Initiatives from government apart, the 1950s saw an early stirring of independent moves which were to develop on several fronts to produce a powerful 'independent' Conservation Movement. Under the umbrella title of the 'Council for Nature' this drew together private and local concerns, often amateur, and sought to affect national policies, not least those regarding woodland. Of special interest was the formation of a series of county naturalists' trusts. That for Leicestershire and Rutland was founded in 1956 and during the first 38 years of its existence it has established 33 reserves including Prior's Coppice and Cloud Wood.

Figure 10.3
Many ancient woodlands in Leicestershire and Rutland have been damaged
through the planting of alien species. As at this site at Burley Wood, Rutland,
areas of semi-natural woodland were replaced by conifers.

As the body charged by law to promote and develop the nation's reserves of wood and timber, the Forestry Commission had planted its one millionth acre by 1956. By 1970 it owned or controlled in England 38% of the total woodland, with the remainder in private hands. Nearly 90% of the trees planted were conifers under a policy of building up timber reserves as quickly and as economically as possible. Post-war plantings of this nature can be seen at the Outwoods near Loughborough, a Domesday woodland site. Yet in spite of all the new planting, by 1970 Great Britain with 7.6%, still remained one of the three least wooded countries in Europe, with only Holland and the Irish Republic having less.[4]

The beginning of the 1970s saw the first signs of a new approach to forestry policy and practice in both public and private sectors. Although the balance of payments and the employment situation were perennial problems, new areas of concern were now recognised. Rising levels of affluence among the general population brought demands for improved leisure-time facilities which, with rapidly increasing individual mobility, brought fresh demands for access to the countryside. Woodlands, it was decided, must cater more for what the public demanded. Recreational facilities were opened up or expanded and the appearance of woodlands would be improved. Mixed plantings would replace many of the depressing plantations of conifers which had been a feature of the Commission's efforts up to that time. In its 'Strategy For The Countryside' (1971) the Leicestershire County Council took up the idea that, among other things related to woodland management, 'the planting programme should where possible aim at producing hard woods as the final stand'.[5] It also proposed a policy of consulting with the Forestry Commission and private owners, with a view to opening up woodland for recreational purposes.[6]

A detailed assessment of the natural history interest of Charnwood Forest (1975) called for a reversal of the unnecessary damage which had been suffered by woodlands and advanced the view for the need for a co-ordinated policy for landscape and wildlife.[7] Yet the Leicestershire Structure Plan, a document published to guide the County's whole development for the following two decades, which was approved in 1976, gave scant regard to woodland in its 109 pages and confined its policy comment on natural history in general to a few vague statements.[8] The 'independent' sector, struggling against such an apparent lack of concern at county level, continued to expand its interests. In 1971 the Leicestershire and Rutland Naturalists' Trust (now the Trust for Nature Conservation, LRTNC) recognised the importance of a further 67 sites (8 of them woodlands) as worthy of SSSI status.

The year 1973 was 'the year of the tree' when the people of Leicestershire and Rutland planted trees in a wave of renewed interest in woodlands. Unfortunately numbers planted were at least equalled by numbers felled as the ravages of Dutch Elm Disease reached their peak. The disease had arrived in the U.K. before 1970

Figure 10.4
The M1 motorway,
like other new
roads in the two
counties, has
damaged several
ancient
woodlands. The
proposed M1
widening scheme
may cause further
destruction.

Figure 10.5
An elm suffering the
the effects of Dutch
elm disease.
As in the rest of
the country, the elms
of Leicestershire and
Rutland have been hit
by the disease since
the 1970s. Elms are
found particularly in
hedgerows and
spinneys, but
woodland trees are
also affected.

and the effects of its presence locally were being noted in 1971. In 1976, the last year when the situation was surveyed, twenty four per cent of those surviving specimens in Leicestershire and Rutland were lost to the fungus.[9] Most of the elms in the two counties had been growing in the hedgerows and in spinneys and their disappearance was noted with great regret by many people over a wide area.

Whatever else it was supposed to achieve the Leicestershire Structure Plan of 1976 was designed to control the large scale changes which were taking place on the landscape. The main themes were the growing motorway system, expansion of the built up area (especially in and around Leicester), provision for leisure facilities and the expansion of mining. In retrospect one marvels that, in a climate of large-scale abandonment of long-held values and ideas about the landscape, so little damage was done to our local woodland. The one major disaster, however, was Buddon Wood where the scale of the enormity became a national scandal.

A census of woodland carried out between the years 1979 and 1982 indicates how the counties' woodland had fared after sixty years of Forestry Commission policies. Once again at a national level only Holland and the Irish Republic were still less wooded than the United Kingdom. In Leicestershire and Rutland there were a little over 19,000 acres of woods. Of this total only 1,730 were coppice-with-standards, 1,977 were coppice, 3,108 scrub and 131 had been recently cleared. The predominant conifer was Norway Spruce and the chief broadleaf was still oak.[10]

By the early 1980s woodland management in the county had virtually ground to a halt. There was little, if any, in-cycle coppice remaining, and the Forestry Commission had largely abandoned the conifer stands unwisely planted in many woods 20 or so years earlier. The heavy clay soils of much of Leicestershire did not suit conifers, which consequently struggled to establish themselves, and many of the woods were far away from the Commission's local office at Fineshade in

Northamptonshire, presenting considerable logistic problems. When later instructed by government to rationalise its operations, the Commission indicated its intention to dispose of most of its properties in Leicestershire by the end of the century. This disposal was to go ahead irrespective of whether the Commission was privatised or not. Considerable concern was felt by conservationists since, despite the fact that the best sites were protected by SSSI status, those in private hands were unlikely to be managed in ways sympathetic to wildlife. By this time the Commission was establishing good conservation practices in other areas, for example in the Rockingham Forest.

Increasing interest in wildlife and the countryside was leading to rapid growth in membership of organisations such as the Leicestershire and Rutland Trust for Nature Conservation, National Trust and Woodland Trust. All these bodies secured sites in the county, including a number of ancient woodlands, and others were acquired by local authorities, trusts and industry. Some were managed for their nature conservation interest, whilst others were not. Swithland Wood, controlled by the Bradgate Park Trust, which remains the most valuable woodland for wildlife in Leicestershire (see Chapter 14), and an extremely popular recreational site, was

Figure 10.6
Former coppice woodland, now derelict. The absence of coppicing has led to this ancient tree becoming top heavy, resulting in the entire stool blowing over. Like this small-leaved lime, many trees will survive such a calamity, and may sprout vigorously along the length of the trunk.

Figure 10.7

Leicestershire and Rutland ancient woodlands managed for their nature conservation interest

Wood	Owner
Brazil Wood	Severn Trent Water
Burbage Wood	Hinckley & Bosworth Borough Council
Burleigh Wood, Loughborough	British Gas
Cloud Wood	LRTNC
Great Merrible Wood	LRTNC
Holywell Wood	British Gas
Martinshaw Wood	Woodland Trust
Outwoods	Charnwood Borough Council
Pickworth Great Wood	Forestry Commission
Polebrook Wood	Woodland Trust
Poultney Wood	LRTNC
Prior's Coppice	LRTNC
Sheepy Wood, Hinckley	Hinckley & Bosworth Borough Council
South Wood	National Trust
Spring Wood, Staunton Harold (in part)	Derbyshire Wildlife Trust
Wardley Wood	Forestry Commission

managed in such ways that the interests of wildlife were barely taken into account. For this retrograde action the Bradgate Park Trust was actually prosecuted by the Nature Conservancy Council – a sad state of affairs. Another important site, Sheet Hedges Wood, owned by Leicestershire County Council, continues to be unmanaged, despite having extensive sycamore invasion. Rides have become restricted and the structure of the wood remains very uniform.

Although further Leicestershire and Rutland woodlands had been notified as SSSIs under the 1981 Wildlife and Countryside Act, statutory protection did not prevent some of them from being neglected and from losing much of their scientific interest. The Nature Conservancy Council was succeeded by English Nature, and the new organisation continued to do what it could to maintain and encourage others to uphold the nature conservation interest of SSSIs. Inadequate legislation and insufficient funding, together with internal re-structuring conspired to make this task a difficult one.

By the early 1990s, however, new grants were being made available to owners by the Forestry Commission. Leicestershire County Council offered stronger protection for woods through its Replacement Structure Plan and Nature Conservation Strategy. Woodland nature reserves were becoming well established, and a major new project, the National Forest, was launched (see following section). At last there were reasons for optimism for the future of woodland in Leicestershire and Rutland.

The National Forest

*F*or centuries Leicestershire and Rutland have been two of the least wooded counties in Britain, but a major project was announced at the start of the 1990s which will, if all goes to plan, dramatically transform this situation. The National Forest, as the project became known, is to be developed over a large part of West Leicestershire, including the Charnwood Forest, extending north and west into Staffordshire, and Derbyshire (see figure 10.8).

It is envisaged that the Forest will be a multi-functional one, with nature conservation and recreation fully integrated with a thriving economy. Only a proportion of the area will be covered by trees, leaving other areas available for ambitious work, for example on extending the area of heathland in Charnwood, and the creation of wetland sites in the Trent valley.

Enlargement of ancient woodlands through natural regeneration of trees on adjacent land was one idea put forward. It was thought this would increase the

Figure 10.8

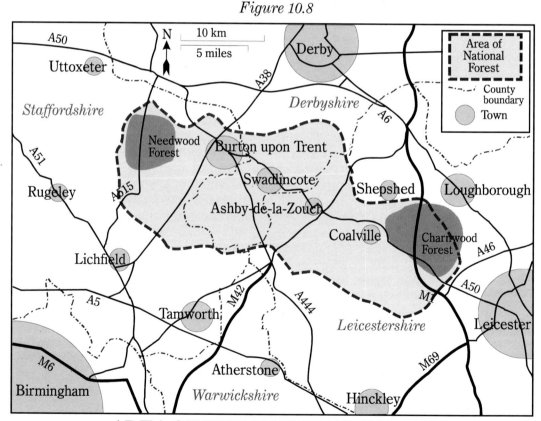

AREA OF THE NATIONAL FOREST

amount of species-rich semi-natural woodland in the Forest, and provide substantial nature conservation benefits. Careful targeting of grants and advice could both enhance the landscape and create large areas of wildlife habitats in a part of Britain where good wildlife sites are few and far between. Species which require large hunting territories, such as red kite and goshawk might again prosper in the region.

Different types of woodland could be developed, using trees native to the Forest area. Mature oak woods could provide habitat for the wood warbler, a rare bird in both Leicestershire and Rutland. Clearings might encourage the nightjar, which has disappeared from the counties in recent years, and the planting of hazel and willow for coppice production would suit many scrub-loving birds such as whitethroat, garden warbler and perhaps nightingale. Special projects could be initiated for the benefit of rare species, such as some of those mentioned, or rare habitats, such as riverside woodland. There is concern amongst conservationists however, that existing good sites in the Forest may be threatened by tree planting. Many of these sites are small and are on so-called 'derelict' land, roadside verges or rough corners of ploughed fields. Moreover, the few remaining good flower meadows are frequently the least productive areas from a landowners point of view, and all of these sites may be targeted for tree planting in preference to the more profitable arable land. In order to satisfy the considerable level of expectation among the public for the rapid growth of the Forest, safeguards for the protection of these existing sites could be overlooked.

A venture of this kind depends upon a firm planning commitment, extending over a long period. If this commitment is given, and provided that conservation is the first consideration in all development and sufficient funds are made available by the government, there is hope that the National Forest could reach its planned potential.

Chapter Eleven
Woodland Wildlife

*F*lowering plants are some of the most conspicuous features of woodland in the spring, with most species blooming between late March and early June. After that the leaves developing on the trees have started to cast a heavy shade on the woodland floor. The floras of individual woods can vary enormously, this often being due to variations in geology or topography.

The woods on the heavy clay soils are dominated by ash, which does not come into leaf until the end of May, allowing colourful shows of plants such as wood anemone, red campion, ramsons, primrose and wood forget-me-not. By contrast the drier, more acidic soils of Charnwood and elsewhere can sometimes form what appears to be a monoculture of bracken beneath an oak dominated canopy. Before the bracken fronds start to appear in May, however, some woods, such as Burley Wood, in Rutland, contain carpets of bluebells.

Since the 18th century botanists have been recording the plant life of Leicestershire woods, and it is clear from the literature that there have been changes in the species composition of the woods, and in the frequency of some of these species. To take one example, a study on the flora of the counties, published in 1933[1] gave detailed species lists for Oakley Wood, which was followed by a study in 1988.[2] Even allowing for variations in the botanists' techniques, and the way they went about their survey, it was obvious that some common species, wood anemone for example, have declined greatly. Furthermore, rarities like herb paris, greater butterfly-orchid, and bird's- nest orchid have disappeared altogether. The rides too are now very species-poor, with plants such as devils-bit scabious, cowslip and betony all gone. All this has probably come about because of the reduced amount of light on the woodland floor and rides, caused by stands of oaks which have matured since the cessation of coppicing, probably early in the 20th century. The influence of modern woodland management and neglect are explored further in chapter 14.

Several plants have become extinct in the two counties during the 20th century, notably the nationally scarce crested cow-wheat, last seen in 1964. A number of others are sufficiently rare to be included in the *Leicestershire Red Data Book*,[3] but comparatively few of our county rarities are woodland species. This is particularly interesting in view of the fact that woodland itself is such a rare habitat in Leicestershire and Rutland. One possible reason is that habitats such as old grassland and heathland are either even rarer, or less robust, suffering more quickly from neglect or inappropriate management.

Much has been written about those flowering plants which have been called 'ancient woodland indicator species', i.e. species which are confined, or nearly so, to ancient woodland.[4] Unfortunately this has led to the popular belief that if certain plants are found in a wood, then that wood must be ancient. In Leicestershire and Rutland at least this is not the case, and there are very few plants which have only been recorded from ancient sites. Some are rarities with too few records from which

Figure 11.1
WOODLAND FLOWERS [5]
Some of the flowers which have an association with ancient woodland.

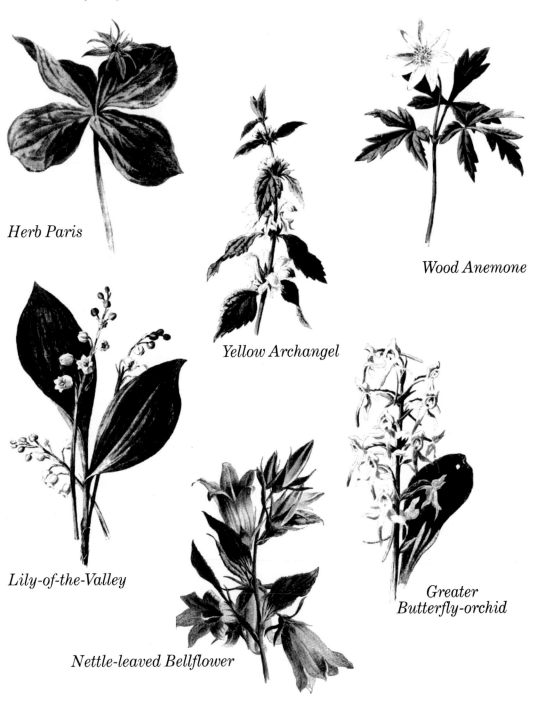

Herb Paris

Wood Anemone

Yellow Archangel

Lily-of-the-Valley

Nettle-leaved Bellflower

Greater
Butterfly-orchid

Figure 11.2

Flowering plants associated with ancient woodland in Leicestershire and Rutland

1. Plants which are strongly associated with ancient woodland.		3. Plants which are only weakly associated with ancient woodland.	
Alder Buckthorn	Pendulous Sedge	Bluebell	Moschatel
Birds-nest Orchid	Purple Small-reed	Dog's Mercury	Primrose
Common Cow-Wheat	Sessile Oak	Early Dog-violet	Ramsons
Crested Cow-Wheat	Small-leaved Lime	Early-purple Orchid	Remote Sedge
Great Wood-rush	Thin-spiked Wood-sedge	Goldilocks Buttercup	Sanicle
Greater Butterfly-orchid	Violet Helleborine	Hairy St. John's-wort	Small Teasel
Herb Paris	Wild Service-tree	Hard Shield-Fern	Wood Sedge
Hairy Wood-rush	Wood Melick		
Lily-of-the-valley	Wood Vetch		
Nettle-leaved Bellflower	Yellow Pimpernel		
2. Plants which are moderately associated with ancient woodland.		**4. Plants more characteristic of secondary woodland**	
Opposite-leaved Golden-saxifrage	Wood Millet	Cleavers	
Smooth-stalked Sedge	Wood Sorrel	Common Nettle	
Toothwort	Wood Speedwell	Cow Parsley	
Wood Anemone	Woodruff	Elder	
	Yellow Archangel		

to draw any real conclusions, but it has been possible from the results of recent fieldwork[6] and a literature search to group species into the four categories used in figure 11.2.

If a particular wood is found to contain a 'suite' of species in the first three categories, this provides a useful clue that it may be old woodland. However additional information from other sources is essential. It is becoming apparent that it is not enough to know that a particular species is recorded for a wood. Its precise location within the wood should be known and this should be plotted against the field evidence of archaeological features, or lack of them, and information from documentary material. It is clear that some, even most, of the counties' larger woods stand on ground much of which has been ploughed or otherwise cleared of trees at some time in the past few hundred years. It is those few areas which have not suffered severe disturbance which act as a 'reserve' for ancient woodland species. Such species may or may not later re-colonise favourable adjacent areas, when these are present.

Plants identified as indicators in other parts of the country do not necessarily work in Leicestershire, and caution in their use is required here. Moreover, even within Leicestershire there appears to be a difference in their behaviour and occurrence between Charnwood Forest and the rest of the county. Wood sorrel, for example, is generally only found in old woodlands outside of Charnwood, but within that area it occurs on heathland in the shade of rocks and walls.

The presence of many small fragments of ancient woodland in the form of hedges and scrub in deep stream valleys can also complicate matters. In the Hallaton area there are some superb linear woodland relics in stream valleys with rich floras containing such good 'indicators' as wood melick and thin-spiked wood-sedge. These valleys adjoin areas of known former woodland.

Planting of some species, especially trees, can also cause confusion. The records of wild service-tree in Leicestershire and Rutland hedgerows may well refer to planted specimens, and examination of the county records of the pendulous sedge reveals that many are from ornamental lakes. Nearly all the others are from ancient woodlands.

A few plants are often abundant in secondary woods, with few other species present. These are also listed in figure 11.2 but it should be noted that they are found in ancient woods too, though usually only sparingly.

Figure 11.3
Clockwise from top left:–
Great Spotted Woodpecker; Nuthatch; Muntjac; Grey Squirrel.

The observation and recording of the variety of animal life of a wood offers no less of a challenge. Many of the mammals are nocturnal, most of the birds shy and the invertebrates are frequently inconspicuous and must be searched for. Once the trees are in leaf there is plenty of cover. Even the major woodlands in Leicestershire and Rutland have not been worked systematically for most of the more obscure groups of invertebrates. As a result most species totals are usually well understated, even at our better known sites. The results of recent survey work at Burley Wood[7] are shown in figure 11.5, but such a list will certainly have missed many of the species that were present.

Before 1700 or so most of the medium and small mammals and birds were either ignored or were considered too difficult to control on a systematic basis in woodland. Domestic grazers apart, damage from deer was the main threat, since rabbits were seldom found in the wild, and the grey squirrel was unknown. The development of sporting firearms in the early 18th century changed the situation dramatically. In particular the larger birds of prey, such as buzzards and red kites, together with the polecat and pine martens and other real and alleged enemies of game birds, were all killed in large numbers. Such treatment extended to herons, crows, owls, red squirrels and even woodpeckers. An example of such destruction can be found in the detailed records of the Burley Estate in Rutland, shown in figure 11.4.[8]

Today, of the mammals, foxes, badgers, stoats, weasels, grey squirrels (which arrived in the 1920s), moles, common and pygmy shrews, field and bank voles and field mice are still common in local woods. Deer remain a problem in some localities, and are discussed in figure 11.6. Several species of bat can be found but they are so difficult to study that much is still unknown about their status and distribution. The dormouse is extremely rare, and it is believed to be confined to just one wood, where it is scarce and thought to be vulnerable to extinction.

In the spring the woods resound to the song of birds. The chaffinch is our commonest woodland bird at that time of the year, though the wren and the robin, which are both susceptible to cold weather, can overtake it after a run of mild winters. Chaffinches remain in the two counties throughout the year, but after the breeding season they move out of the woods to feed on farmland. They start to return in March, when the males sing loudly on sunny mornings, particularly on the

Figure 11.4[8]

Mammals and birds killed on the Burley Estate, Rutland 1807-16

Buzzards	285	Crows	1,603	Polecats	206
Red Kites	183	Jackdaws	1,798	Pine Martens	9
Hawks	340	Herons	24	Cats	554
Owls	386	Woodpeckers	103	Red Squirrels	197
Magpies	1,530	Stoats	1,269	Rats	17,108
Jays	428	Weasels	454	Mice	20,734

Figure 11.5

Burley Wood - Number of different species identified as present

Vascular plants	279	False scorpions	2
Bryophytes (liverworts and mosses)	73	Harvestmen	6
Fungi	155	Beetles	183
Lichens	122	Butterflies	23
Mammals	20 or more	Moths	34
Birds	76 (45 breeding)	Flies	134
Reptiles and amphibians	5	Dragonflies	3
Molluscs (slugs and snails)	19	Grasshoppers	4
Flatworms	1	Plant bugs	2
Earthworms	6	Lacewings & allies	1
Centipedes	7	Bees, wasps & ants	2
Millipedes	16		

n.b. Moths, beetles and flies would actually number several hundred species each, and others of the group, such as bees, wasps, ants, plant bugs and lacewings are also drastically under-recorded. The list is of positive identifications, rather than a complete list of the species present.

warm south facing margins. They raise just one brood of young and then leave the woodland in midsummer.

The occurrence and distribution of birds in woodland is influenced by many factors, but particularly structure. Mature *high forest* (a woodland composed of mature trees, which will include old and dead trees) is a rare habitat indeed, and in Leicestershire there is little woodland which meets this description. This is a consequence of coppice management in historic times, a practice which did not encourage the retention of old standard trees. Since the decline of coppicing stands of mature trees have started to develop, as at Burley Wood and Southwood. These suit birds which require high forest such as woodpeckers, redstart and nuthatch. The last named species was restricted until quite recently to those parts of the county where mature woodland was found (mainly in Charnwood, the Vale of Belvoir and central Rutland), but a dramatic expansion to many areas has occurred, perhaps as a result of the gradual maturing of neglected coppice.

The interior of old and neglected coppice is only frequented by a few species of birds, including robins and wrens, which do not appear to have exacting habitat requirements. Other species like the garden warbler, occur along rides and on the wood edge. Figure 11.7 shows the distribution of three species with differing habitat preferences in Prior's Coppice.

Woodland management over the centuries has also had a profound effect on the populations of species of invertebrates. Locally the three most studied groups

Figure 11.6 The Threat from Deer

Deer are a major threat to ancient woodland in the 1990s. The problem comes from the increasing numbers and expansion in ranges of several species of deer, which can browse young trees and regenerating coppice. Coppicing in particular becomes almost impossible to practise, since protection of panels involves very expensive fences (electric or otherwise), although stools can be protected to varying degrees with, for example, dead hedges, or brash.

There are just two species of deer native to Britain - red and roe. Neither occurs in a wild state in Leicestershire, although the former are kept in Donington and Bradgate Parks, and there is a deer farm at Arnesby. Roe deer are reported to be spreading towards Leicestershire from the east, and may colonise in due course.

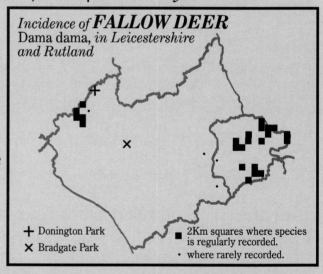

Incidence of **FALLOW DEER**
Dama dama, *in Leicestershire and Rutland*

+ Donington Park
× Bradgate Park

■ 2Km squares where species is regularly recorded.
· where rarely recorded.

The two species that are firmly established in the county are fallow (an ancient introduction to England) and muntjac. Fallow are localized, the map showing their distribution. They are often abundant where they do occur. In the north-west, herds of up to 24 have been seen in Southwood, for example, and in North-East Rutland herds of 200 have been reported, incredible as that may seem. Muntjac are more widespread, but are never as obvious on account of their less gregarious habits and small size. They also do not appear to cause as much damage as the larger species.

Damage to woodland from fallow deer is evident wherever they are found. In Southwood browse lines on holly trees can be seen, and in Pickworth Great Wood the great wood-rush grows more luxuriantly where it is more difficult for deer to reach it. Although there is no evidence to show that this deer species is extending its range in Leicestershire, the concern that this might happen is a deterrent to any owner who might be considering re-introducing coppicing. A programme to reduce the population is required if the woodlands in areas already inhabited by fallow deer are not to be irrevocably damaged.

THE DISTRIBUTION OF THREE BIRD SPECIES WITHIN PRIOR'S COPPICE

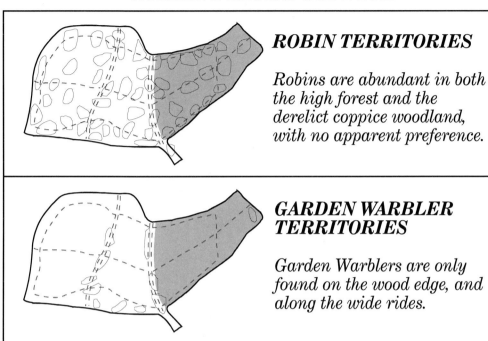

ROBIN TERRITORIES

Robins are abundant in both the high forest and the derelict coppice woodland, with no apparent preference.

GARDEN WARBLER TERRITORIES

Garden Warblers are only found on the wood edge, and along the wide rides.

NUTHATCH TERRITORIES

Nuthatches occur only in the high forest area.

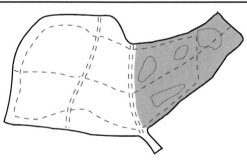

- - - - - - - Wide rides
- - - - - - Narrow rides and paths

High forest area

Bird territory

500m

500 yards

N

Figure 11.7

Woodland birds are strongly influenced by the structure of the habitat. Prior's Coppice contains two areas with rather different management histories. The larger part is ash dominated derelict coppice, last felled around the 1940s, and currently being brought back into cycle. The remainder has been left untouched for considerably longer, such that it is now a high forest habitat, with many mature oaks. The bird life of the two areas is markedly different, and well demonstrates the impact of management. The maps show how the territories of three bird species were distributed within Prior's Coppice in 1993.

*Duke of Burgundy
Fritillary*

White Admiral

Large Tortoiseshell

Pearl-bordered Fritillary

Dark Green Fritillary

Leg Williams

Silver-washed Fritillary

Figure 11.8
Lost butterflies, not seen in Leicestershire or Rutland for several decades.

of insects are the butterflies, moths and beetles. Unfortunately the neglect of many local woodlands over the last few decades has meant that the true woodland butterflies have suffered badly, as glades and rides which these species require have become overgrown. At Owston Woods, for example, 29 species had been recorded up to 1976, but only 16 have been seen since. Those lost include the duke of Burgundy; white admiral; large tortoiseshell; pearl-bordered fritillary; dark green fritillary; and the silver-washed fritillary.

Many species of beetles have equally demanding requirements for survival. They have no powers of spreading or the ability to adapt to new sources of wood.

*Scolytus
the bark beetle*

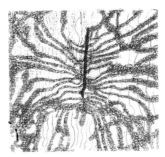

*Extensive tunnels or
'galleries' produced by
feeding larvae*

Bark beetle larvae feeding within the bark

*Figure 11.9
Scolytus bark beetle. Many different beetles inhabit the bark of mature
trees, and generally cause little damage. Unfortunately the elm bark
beetle, Scolytus scolytus, is the carrier of Dutch elm disease fungus,
which has ravaged the countryside since the 1970s.*

When the specialized habitat disappears the beetles disappear with it. In Leicestershire and Rutland some study has been carried out on those species associated with decaying heartwood in trees in ancient wood – mainly pasture woodland. The presence of such species in the parks of Bradgate, Donington and in Buddon Wood is hardly surprising. The presence of *Lathridius consomilis* in Southwood and, in 1904, of *Abdera quadri-fasciata* at Ambion Wood also indicates the long association of these areas with woodland.[9]

The same broad considerations which suggest both flowering plants and insects as possible indicators of old woodland also apply to spiders. Much of the study of species associated with oakwoods has been carried out in southern England. Many species which occur commonly in the south are absent or rare in Leicestershire and Rutland, and in comparison our two counties have fewer species, reflecting the relative poverty of ancient woodland. The table in Figure 11.10 lists 13 species of spider which are indicators of sites which have been continuously wooded over long periods.[10]

Figure 11.10

Incidence of SPIDER SPECIES observed in fifteen Leicestershire and Rutland Woods	Outwoods	Buddon Wood	Swithland Wood	Owston Wood	Stoneywell Wood	Burbage Wood	Sheet Hedges Wood	Great Merrible Wood	Bardon Hill Wood	Briery Wood	Cloud Wood	Nailstone Wiggs	Stoke Dry Wood	Grace Dieu Wood	Ambion Wood
Agroeca brunnea	◆	◆													
Anyphaena accentuata			◆	◆	◆	◆									◆
Xysticus lanio							◆								
Haplodrassus silvestris		◆													
Ballus chalybeius		◆													
Cyclosa conica		◆													
Saloca diceros				◆		◆	◆								
Lepthyphantes tenebricola		◆	◆		◆			◆							
Atea sturmi		◆								◆	◆				
Achaearanea lunata		◆				◆						◆			
Gibbaranea gibbosa								◆							
Asthenargus paganus					◆				◆			◆	◆		
Pachgnatha listeri												◆		◆	

Of particular interest from this data are records from Nailstone Wiggs and Burbage Wood. The former wooded area, first recorded in 1392,[11] has a continuous history as a woodland until very recently when the (then) National Coal Board used it as a dump for coal stocks. Burbage Wood, looked at in detail in chapter thirteen, has been shown to be almost, but not entirely, secondary woodland.

Clearly, much work needs to be done on the many unknown aspects of the animal life of our local woodlands, before it is too late. In particular the confirmation or otherwise of the continued presence of species first noted by naturalists of the last century should not be neglected. This contributes much to the understanding of woodland history in our fast-changing local landscape.

Chapter Twelve

Classifying Woodlands

The wildwood which once undoubtedly covered the flood plains, the lighter limestones and the sandstone soils has now all disappeared and it is not possible to determine its precise nature and composition. Our remaining ancient woodland is mostly situated on heavy clay or the poor soils on the old rocks of Charnwood. But as we have seen in earlier chapters, it has been subjected to a high degree of manipulation by local people.

Figure 12.1

MAIN AREAS OF SEMI-NATURAL WOODLAND
showing the main woodland types present in each area.

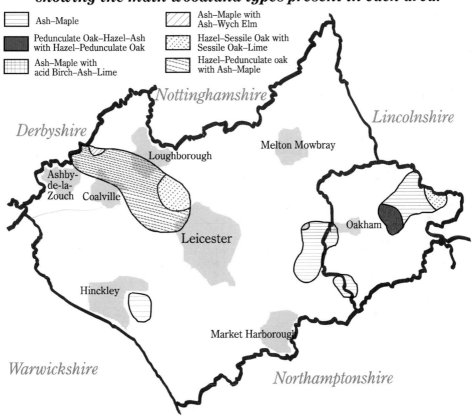

Ash–Maple

Pedunculate Oak–Hazel–Ash with Hazel–Pedunculate Oak

Ash–Maple with acid Birch–Ash–Lime

Ash–Maple with Ash–Wych Elm

Hazel–Sessile Oak with Sessile Oak–Lime

Hazel–Pedunculate oak with Ash–Maple

By the 20th century ancient woodland in Leicestershire and Rutland was almost entirely confined to the areas shown on the map. A survey carried out in the 1980s[1] identified the main stand types, using Peterken's classification.[2] These are indicated in a simplified form.

Only about 2% of Leicestershire and Rutland is now covered by ancient woodland and just half of that has been largely unaffected by planting, and can be described as *semi-natural.*[3] This woodland is concentrated into discrete areas which are characterised by distinct plant communities, as shown in Figure 12.1. The map, and those in the following chapter, show the community types developed by George Peterken.[2]

More recently the National Vegetation Classification has been developed,[4] and details of this system are given in appendix two. It uses an even more detailed ecological classification, and any one wood may contain a number of different such communities.

At a much more general level, the different types of woodland found in the county can be described under the following broad headings:

Ash Woodland

Ash is the dominant tree in much of Leicestershire, being abundant everywhere except on the drier, more acid soils of Charnwood and parts of the coalfield. This dominance is reflected in many of the county's ancient woodlands e.g. Asplin and Breedon Cloud Woods.

Figure 12.2
Ash woodland at Owston Woods.

A canopy dominated by ash provides only relatively light shade over the shrub and field layers, and woods of this type tend to have rich floras. Where oak is co-dominant the combination of heavier shade and a leaf litter that decomposes only slowly produces a less species-rich field layer; brambles and bluebells are often abundant with little else in association.

These woods have frequently been called oak-ash woods.[5] This may once have been an apt description, but oak is now only occasional or even rare in some woods, especially in those woods which were clear-felled during or soon after the Second World War. Natural regeneration of oak is now unusual on the heavy calcareous clays, and its past abundance may well have been due to deliberate planting. Where woodland escaped clear-felling, as in part of Prior's Coppice, the flora is noticeably poorer than in that part which was clear-felled, and now contains little oak (see the next chapter).

Ash is the dominant tree of the woods in East Leicestershire around Launde. Owston Woods are conspicuously the most diverse of these woods, and also the most species-rich.

In West Leicestershire wych elm is sometimes frequent in the ash woods, which have a slightly different ground flora from the ash woods in the east. Pendulous sedge, for example, is almost absent in the east but frequent in the west.

Small-leaved lime is rare in the ash woods, probably only occurring as a native tree at Owston, where it is found in clusters of giant coppice stools, apparently of great age.

Oak Woodland

*T*rue oakwoods are confined in Leicestershire and Rutland to the more acid soils. In the Charnwood Forest both native species of oak occur, often together with the hybrid, as in Swithland Wood. Sessile oak is an ancient woodland tree in the Forest, and it is the pedunculate oak which forms secondary woodland when given the opportunity. Seedlings appear in abundance in some years. Small-leaved lime is associated with the oaks in both Buddon and Swithland Woods, and holly, rowan and silver birch are all frequent. Birch can become abundant in clear-felled oakwoods, but otherwise the shrub layer is often sparse, with a field layer dominated by bluebells and brambles. Lime-hating species such as great wood-rush, wood sage and creeping soft-grass are all frequent.

Both oaks can also be found in the ancient woods of the coalfield in the north west of Leicestershire, but the ground flora in these woods is not as varied as the woods of Charnwood. The woods of both of these areas are now developing into high forest, and there are some fine stands of oak to be seen, especially in Swithland Wood and Southwood.

Pedunculate oak is the dominant tree of a small group of woods in central Rutland, and Burley Wood in particular contains some magnificent specimens. Natural regeneration of oak is frequent here, but other than hazel and silver birch (and locally ash and field maple) other trees and shrubs are not common. The ground

Figure 12.3
Oak woodland at Burley Wood.

flora is species-poor too, though there are impressive displays of bluebells in the spring.

The final area of oak woodland is on the border between Rutland and Lincolnshire, where sessile oak is the most frequent tree in Newall Wood, a wood standing on glacial sand and gravel. Sessile oak has also been recorded in the past in other woods in North East Rutland, but access to these woods is now difficult to obtain, and it is not known whether the species is still present.

Alder Woodland

*A*lder is almost entirely restricted to the banks of streams and marshy ground in Leicestershire and Rutland. Since there are few streams or marshes in the remaining ancient woodland in the counties, it is not surprising that alder is an uncommon tree in this habitat. However, where it is found it forms a very distinctive type of woodland. Characteristic species are opposite-leaved golden-saxifrage, meadowsweet and guelder-rose, all of which can be abundant.

Where marshy ground forms, as in Grace Dieu, Swithland and Skeffington Woods, the ground flora can be very rich. Wood anemones are sometimes abundant, and other attractive herbs include marsh-marigold, primrose and marsh valerian.

Wood horsetail is frequent in the wet alderwood at Grace Dieu, and there is a stand of common reed at Skeffington. Only in Owston Woods and Southwood does alder occur on drier, level ground, forming very small stands of what has been called *'plateau alderwood'*.[5]

Figure 12.4
Alder woodland at Owston Woods.

Elm Woodland

*O*n the more base-rich, wetter soils of East Leicestershire, Rutland and the Hinckley district, suckering elms produce dense thickets. Standing and fallen dead timber is common, resulting from Dutch elm disease, and since common nettle and brambles are often abundant in the field layer, this type of woodland is frequently almost impenetrable in midsummer. Despite the continuing effects of Dutch elm disease, there is no shortage of vigorous young elm suckers in the woods, showing that the disease may not kill the rootstock. Both English elm and small-leaved elm are present, in addition to hybrids with wych elm.

Chapter Thirteen
Six Woodlands

CLOUD, PASTURE and ASPLIN WOODS, BREEDON

*I*n Domesday Book Breedon and Wilson were included under Tonge, and a large woodland measuring one league by half a league is recorded. The single entry does not seem to have included two other known twelfth century wooded areas in the manor.[1] These were Brunhaga Wood and Westwode. They were most likely different parts of one wood and known collectively as the 'Wood of Breedon', which lay in the west against the border with Derbyshire. In addition, the existence of a third wooded area, to the north east of Breedon, is indicated by field name evidence.[2] The probable existence in the eleventh century of part or all of the present Asplin Wood must also be considered a strong possibility.

The first record for Cloud Wood is 1226 when Robert de Tatershall, Lord of Breedon, attempted to enclose his woods of *'Cludes'* and *'Hirstes'*, which lay 'in Tonge', as a deer park. He was challenged by Simon de Roppesley of Worthington who claimed that the move would deprive him of his common grazing in the woods.[3] The outcome was an agreement whereby Robert should enclose the woods with a fence as a park for ever but would allow Simon free pannage therein for 20 pigs and the right to take one buck and one doe per year. Furthermore Simon and his men of Worthington, 'free as well as villeins', were to have common grazing in the park for their cattle and a gate was made 'in the foreign wood of Tonge' for the regulation of the beasts.[4]

Field survey has revealed surviving fragments of the original park pale along its line of greatest extent. These are shown on figure 13.1. The present boundaries of Cloud Wood, though old, are not those of the early thirteenth century. The southern line of the park pale is *'fossilized'* in the wood, the north edge of which must have extended to the north of the course of Stocking (land cleared of tree stumps) Lane. At the same time the southern edge of the wood extended further towards Worthington. Cloud Wood today, the site of the quarry included, extends over approximately 150 acres. In 1656 it contained 140 acres,[5] in 1772 150 acres[6] and in 1873 146 acres.[7] The present boundaries were probably determined long before the mid 17th century, however, and probably represent, among other things, the minimum area below which successive generations found it impracticable or uneconomic to plough or otherwise cultivate. The presence of the ancient medieval wood and park, the lack of other archaeological features together with the rich flora and fauna also indicate the long continuity as a woodland site.

Pasture and Asplin Woods, probably as rich in wildlife as Cloud Wood, present a very different history. The principle features are shown on figure 13.1. Most striking within the ancient wood banks is the large area of ridge and furrow in Pasture Wood and its total absence from Asplin. Here is a firm indication that most

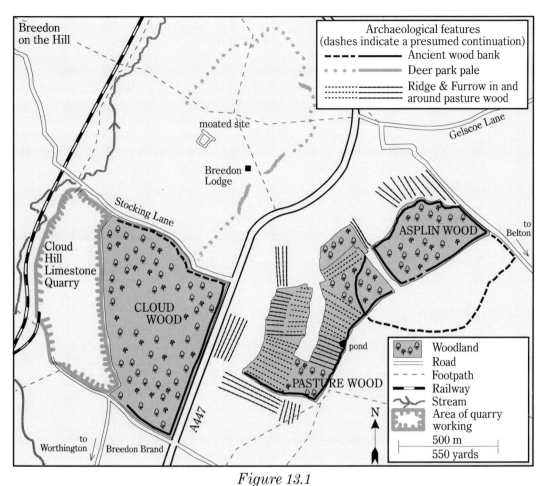

Figure 13.1

CLOUD, PASTURE and ASPLIN WOODS, BREEDON

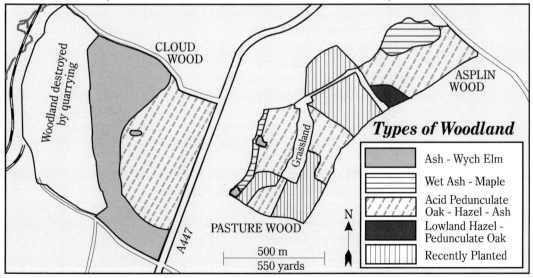

of the former has been ploughed at one time or another. The ridges and furrows are difficult to detect and probably represent ploughing over a relatively short period. The richness of the flora of these areas appears to be no different from that in the undisturbed area, thus indicating the feature is very old and has been out of use for a long time. A 15th century record identifies at least part of Pasture Wood as 'dame Emma Rydding'.[8] *'Ryding'* or *'Ridding'* means land rid of trees and the Dame in question is presumably Emma Tatershall (wife of Adam Gailly) who died in 1306.[9]

The north-west portion of Pasture Wood, now a young plantation and overgrown with brambles, contains a major ancient woodland bank which once formed the boundary between the two woods and the furthest extent of medieval ploughing.

In the mid seventeenth century Pasture Wood, under the name Hannibal Riding, occupied about 50 acres whilst 'Tong Aspland' covered about 20.[10] In 1772 the figures were 51 and 32 acres respectively.[11] By 1873, 'Great Aspinall Wood' had 59 acres and 'Little Aspinall Wood' had 34.[12] Both figures correspond to their present sizes. In the 18th century both woods extended in irregular form beyond the north-east boundary into an elongated open area of common grazing known as Tongue Pasture.[13] This site was the remaining patch of the broad band of Boulder Clay on which the two woodlands stand.

The Domesday Book record for Tonge (which also included Wilson and Breedon) translates as approximately 600 acres of woodland. Even allowing for the other woodlands which may be included in this total it is clear that the eleventh century woodland extended over a wider area than the total accounted for by the present Cloud, Pasture and Asplin Woods. The lack of evidence for such a large quantity of 'missing' woodland elsewhere suggests that the Cloud area is the location. The irregular shape of the manor here, a pronounced tongue of land southwards suggests a special use, in this case woodland and wood pasture, where the cattle of the people of Breedon found common grazing with those of the people of Worthington and elsewhere. The soil is mostly Boulder Clay, wet and intractable. Part of the area had always been known as *the Brand*, possibly 'land cleared by burning', or more likely 'land where charcoal was made'. In 1392 ten acres of arable were granted 'lying in le Brendes, alias the breches' (land newly broken).[14] Sixteenth century records show the presence of patches of woodland now disappeared, and other small inclosures from the common.[15] In short, it seems likely that part or all the present wooded area of Cloud and probably Asplin represents part of the Domesday Wood of Tonge and has carried wood continuously for at least nine centuries. Pasture Wood, too, should probably be included as a very ancient site but, as has been seen, cannot claim the same lack of disturbance over the same period.

There has been a long and continuous practice of coppicing in Cloud Wood. Deer parks very often contained areas of coppiced wood which also provided pasture for the deer. In 1677 the wood was let for grazing after the coppice 'had been seven years cut'.[16] Today some ancient stools of two hundred or more years survive but most of the extensive coppice has been much neglected.

The foregoing remarks on the history of the area go some way towards explaining why these woods together form one of the richest areas of woodland for flowering plants and ferns in Leicestershire. The underlying geology is sufficiently varied to have resulted in a flora with plants typical of both calcareous and acid soils, with many thought to be associated with ancient woodland in the county.

Triassic Mercian mudstone dominates the geology of much of west Leicestershire, but in some parts it is overlain by Boulder Clay, and at Breedon we have three woods developed mainly on the latter. The Boulder Clay here is not as wet or sticky as that found in East Leicestershire, all too well known to anyone who has walked those woods. Being derived from less calcareous rocks, the Boulder Clay in the west carries a flora with species typical of more acid soils, pendulous sedge for example, which is often abundant. Sanicle, and other species which do not appear to like the heavy, frequently water-logged soils of the east, are common in the woods at Breedon.

Another important feature of the geology of the Breedon area is the Carboniferous Limestone. Cloud Wood was until comparatively recently the only ancient woodland in Leicestershire with a significant stand of semi-natural woodland growing on this substrate. All of this part of the wood has now been destroyed by quarrying operations, and the integrity of this superb woodland has been damaged further by dumping of quarry waste on the rides, so that they now stand several feet higher than the woodland floor. A number of plants which once used to occur in Cloud Wood, notably yellow star-of-Bethlehem, probably grew on the limestone and no longer appear to be present.

Ash is the dominant tree of these woods, though it grows with many others to form what is in places a wonderfully rich and varied tree and shrub layer. Pedunculate oak is locally frequent, as are, to name just a few, hazel, holly, silver

Figure 13.2 Wood anemones in Pasture Wood, Breedon.

birch, wild cherry, wych elm, dogwood, field maple and aspen. Asplin Wood gets its name from the aspen tree, and it is a wood with a particularly fine structure. It is clearly an old coppice that has not been managed in the traditional way for several decades, and is now developing a high forest structure through natural regeneration. The coppice stools that can still be seen are not especially big, but there are already oak and ash standards up to about 200 years of age present. Cloud Wood, on the other hand, looks to have been clear-felled not more than about 50 years ago, and consequently has a more uniform structure.

Asplin Wood shows an interesting change in vegetation from species-rich ash-field maple woodland with many calcicolous (lime loving) species in the north, where Boulder Clay occurs, through to relatively species-poor pendunculate oak-hazel woodland, with calcifuge (lime hating) plants such as hairy wood-rush, in the south-west. (See map of woodland types in Figure 13.1.) Here there is no Boulder Clay over the mudstone.

Figure 13.3
Breedon Quarry and Cloud Wood, from the west. Pasture and Asplin woods
can also be seen in the middle left of the picture.

The ground flora of these woods produces spectacular displays of colour in the spring, with many common woodland plants, such as wood anemones, occurring in profusion. Early-purple orchid and greater butterfly-orchid, woodruff and yellow archangel are just a few less common plants that can be seen in remarkable abundance, but it is noticeable that some areas are richer than others. Asplin and Cloud Woods are undoubtedly the most valuable for woodland plants, leading one to suspect that Pasture Wood is poorer because it was once under the plough. However, there are good populations of herb paris and greater butterfly-orchid in this wood, both scarce Leicestershire plants. These two species are poor colonisers in this part of the country, and it is interesting that they are found here on ridge and furrow. It is likely that these species re-colonised from the surrounding woodland when the medieval ploughland was abandoned. In recent times Pasture Wood has suffered from planting with conifers and broadleaves, and this has also probably had an adverse effect on the ground flora.

Pasture Wood does contain a strip of old grassland within the woodland (see figure 13.1), and it seems likely that the wood derives its present name from this. Apparently a field at one time, it still has the remains of a fence along one of the long sides. Large numbers of common spotted-orchids, smaller numbers of heath spotted-orchids, as well as the uncommon pale sedge, can all be found here. This is undoubtedly the best remaining example of woodland grassland in West Leicestershire.

Note that access to Cloud Wood is restricted to members of the Leicestershire and Rutland Trust for Nature Conservation, except on public open days. Pasture and Asplin Woods are privately owned and have no public access. See appendix one for details of woodlands with public access.

BUDDON WOOD

Until recently this wooded area formed a very prominent feature of the Charnwood skyline, rising as a tree-covered dome of granite to the west of the valley of the Soar.

At the time of Domesday Book, Buddon formed part of the woodland of some 400 acres of the manor of Barrow, the remainder being accounted for by un-named woodland of the manorial waste of the interior of Charnwood Forest.[17] Some time before the year 1135 Buddon had become incorporated into the hunting park of the earl of Chester. Shortly after the death in 1273 of Roger de Somery, the park and wood were partitioned between his four heiresses and in 1309 oaks, aspens and alders were growing at Buddon. Seventy years later part of the wood contained oaks, ash, beech, elm and willow.[18]

Late in the middle ages a considerable part of the wood was acquired by purchase and exchange by the Erdington family from whom it eventually passed to the Hastings, earls of Huntingdon, of Ashby-de-la-Zouch. In 1629 the 5th earl leased the wood under strict terms for 21 years for a total of £133, when oaks, ashes, alders, thorns and hollies were involved.[19] In 1654 the 6th earl sold his part of Buddon to Peter Cheveney for £2,100.[20] From the Cheveneys the wood passed by purchase to Sir Joseph Danvers of Swithland.[21]

A second part of the wood, the *'Kendal Buddon'* of the records, which lay to the south of the Cheveney purchase, passed from de Somery's descendants through several different families before becoming part of the estate of William Danvers of Swithland in 1632.[22]

The two remaining sections of Buddon have largely undocumented histories before the eighteenth century when they returned to the Danvers of Swithland. Thus, by 1770, the entire wood once again returned to the ownership of one family in whose hands it, or what is left of it, remains today.[23]

The prominent nature of the hill together with the beauty of its pristine spring greenness was a delight for travellers along the A6 in the nineteenth century. The geology and topography of the area are the factors which governed the Wood's survival to the late twentieth century. The granite core was covered in most places by a very shallow layer of largely acid soil which in places was entirely absent, as the ancient rocks outcropped at the surface. Elsewhere deep accumulations of peat and humus could be found. In spite of the unpromising conditions, individual trees, especially oaks, of the natural woodland sometimes reached a great size. It seems that the more favoured parts of the wood were given over to grazing and that the present boundaries contain the area which, since the end of the twelfth century, has represented the smallest area of uncultivable land.

The earliest signs of human activity on Buddon are indicated by finds of flint blades, cones and endscrapers which date from the mesolithic period (c.12,000 to 3,000 BC) and which suggest an occupation site on the Hill. Bronze Age pottery of the post-Deveral Rimbury Tradition has also been found here suggesting a settlement in the eighth century BC.[24]

Figure 13.4 Buddon Wood before quarrying commenced in the early 1970s.

Figure 13.5

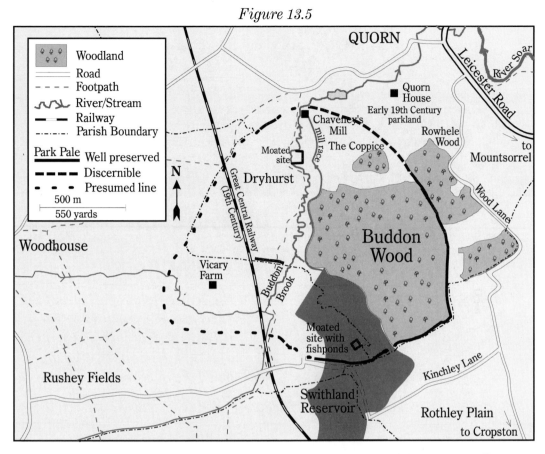

BUDDON WOOD BEFORE QUARRYING COMMENCED
(showing the area enclosed by Barrow medieval park)

It is clear that Buddon supported woodland cover in one form or another over much of its present area without a break from at least 1086 (and probably very long before that) to the present century. Of considerable archaeological interest is the ancient wood bank which marks the eastern and southern edges of the present wood. This bank acted as both wood boundary and park pale and in its latter function it can be traced, in muted form, across the early nineteenth century park created around Quorn House. To the south it has been discovered below the waters of the late nineteenth century Swithland Reservoir. The flooding of the Buddon Brook also caused the destruction of a small strip of the wood along its south-west edge.

Until the Second World War Buddon Wood was dominated by magnificent stands of sessile oaks, while small-leaved lime was locally frequent. During the war the wood was clear-felled and allowed to regenerate naturally. Silver birch became abundant while many of the sessile oaks, and smaller numbers of limes, produced coppice growth. Other trees occurred in varying numbers. The wood still contained much of its important fauna and flora until about 1950.

County Council gave quarrying go-ahead

FATE OF BUDDON WOOD SEALED 20 YEARS AGO

Over 50 years ago the Mountsorrel Granite Co. obtained a lease from the owners of the greater part of the wood to quarry granite. In the 1950's they applied and were granted planning permission to q u a r r y the major portion of the wood. This unfortunate decision of the County Council is at the base of the disaster that faces the wood today.

Buddon Wood: Whitehall pressure on 1946 planners

THE planners who in 1946 considered for s e v e n months the appplication to quarry Buddon Wood viewed it "with concern" and gave the now contro-versial permission only in the face of pressure from Whitehall.

Slap in the champions of Buddon face for Buddon

A SLAP in the eye to the Buddon Wood Preservation Society was given yester-day when the County Council threw out a move calling for fresh thinking on a proposed agreement with the quarry company.

Figure 13.6
The Battle for Buddon Wood

Contemporary reports from the Leicester Mercury reflect the helplessness of both planners and public in attempting to block the quarry.
Top: 20th December 1971
Middle: 18th February 1972
Bottom: 11th May 1972

Figure 13.7
Buddon Wood in 1978.

*Figure 13.8
Buddon wood in
1989*

Then tragedy struck. Unfortunately the granite on which Buddon Wood stood had great value as roadstone. Permission to quarry the site had been granted in the 1940s, when nature conservation was in its infancy and environmental considerations were scarcely taken into account by planning authorities. Despite the protests of conservationists and an outcry from the general public, the great wood made way for the largest man-made hole in Europe.

Although the integrity of this wonderful wood has been shattered, a band of trees remains around the edge of the quarry. It is vital that this band be left because it still holds many of the animals and plants found in the former more extensive woodland. Moreover, it could act as a reservoir from which species might one day be able to spread into woodland that could develop in the worked out quarry.

Sessile oak and small-leaved lime are still frequent in the remaining woodland, and both have clearly been coppiced in the past as some large stools are present. Pedunculate oak occurs in some areas, as do colonies of alder, wych elm and aspen. Sycamore is invading the stands and is abundant in places. The shrub layer is generally fairly open, containing hazel and holly, with bramble abundant beneath.

The ground flora is not as rich as it once was. Bracken is abundant, while other plants which occur locally and in small quantities include heather, wavy hair-grass, bluebell and wood sage.

More woodland plants have been recorded at Buddon Wood than at any other woodland site in Leicestershire and Rutland, and more rare species have been recorded also. Many have not been seen for a long time, for example herb paris. A few, including common cow-wheat, lily-of-the-valley, goldenrod and the nationally scarce spreading bellflower, are still present.

The plunder of Buddon has meant the local extinction of many species of wildlife, among them the magnificent red wood ant which was once abundant here. Clearly, for our two counties the destruction of Buddon has proved to be the wildlife disaster of the century. Its passing, and the circumstances leading to it, make this wood one of the most potent symbols for the need for conservation anywhere.

BURBAGE and SHEEPY WOODS

*B*urbage Wood (49 acres) and Sheepy Wood (33 acres) form part of the public recreational area of 190 acres known as Burbage Common, situated two miles north-east of Hinckley. Both woods and the grassland around them are situated on Boulder Clay which produces water-logging in winter.

Domesday Book notes at Burbage a wood measuring half a league by four furlongs which is approximately 200 modern acres. That the wood was held subject to common rights is indicated by mid-thirteenth century records. In 1247 Hugh de Peters claimed common pasture in the wood of Henry Hastings at Burbage in respect of his free tenement in Aston [Flamville].[25] Again in 1261, John Mansell, the rector of the church of Barwell, claimed reasonable *estover* (the right to take wood for repairs) in the same Henry's Wood as well as common of pasture.[26] However, the woodland was in decline. A survey of the manor of Burbage in 1289 records fields called *'stocking'* and *'breach',* the former a sure sign of woodland removal.[27] Although no woodland is mentioned at this time, the right of pannage was still exercised in the manor. In 1335, the woodland of Burbage was valued at only 40s. which seems an under-estimate considering the acreage which must have existed at the time.[28] When Agnes Hastings died in 1368 she held an enclosed wood containing about 100 acres where the herbage was worth 30s.[29]

There are no records of woodland in Burbage for the next century and a half. At the death of Katherine Grey in 1509 it was stated that during her husband's lifetime he (George, the second earl of Kent) had held 200 acres of wood in the manor.[30] The Greys leased their woodland to a number of local people but the terms of the leases speak of its disappearance. In 1513 a 'wood' called Great Stocking contained 200 acres of pasture but no woodland is mentioned or implied. Thomas Rumbolde's lease of 1606 records '66 acres of pasture or converted ground', this in an area which has come down to the present as the place-name *'Rumbles Wood'.*[31] Other early seventeenth century leases emphasise pasture in woodland or pasture in areas 'converted' or 'late wooded'. Thomas Armston leased pasture extending over 108 acres on the 'nether side of park wood (late wood)'. There were in addition 12 acres in Stocking Meadow and an undisclosed acreage in 'Lash Wood (late Wood ground)'[32]. Three leases of 1620 name closes which refer to former woodland. Robert Watkins and Richard Barnewell leased 'part of park wood, ground adjacent stocking meadow'.[33] Thomas Adcock had 'his parcel of Park Wood Ground, by Burbage Lane' whilst Thomas Rumbolde had 'part of park wood ground next Hinckley Field'.[34] Leases of 1628 and 1634 refer to 'Stocking woods adjacent the Smenell' and 'coppice wood called the Outwoods adjoining the Common'.[35] A little later, two coppice woods were leased, one 'adjacent Smenell and Smenell Lane', the other 'adjoining the common, commonly called the Outwoods'.[36]

Early eighteenth century leases refer to closes having woodland names but lacking actual woodland, but the manorial accounts speak of other areas of well maintained and carefully managed woodland. In 1708/09 underwood, ash poles, faggots, oak poles and oak faggots from 'Burbage Woods' made a total of £56.15s.2d.[37] Two woods were involved, one the Coppice Wood and the other the Spring Wood. The value of their products in 1712 was £131.2s.3d. less expenses for cutting of £7.9s.3d.[38] In 1716 the Coppice Wood 'of which about one acre and a half is good pasture' enclosed a little over 33 acres. The Spring Wood 'in two parts' enclosed about 50 acres.[39]

John Prior marks both Burbage and Sheepy Woods on his map of 1777. He also shows the adjacent Aston Firs, providing the first record for this wood.[40] In the description of his tour of Leicestershire, published in 1790, John Throsby mentions Burbage Wood and notes it was still in the hands of the descendants of the Greys.[41] From 1835, the date of the first edition of the One Inch Ordnance Survey Map, all three woods have remained more or less unchanged in area to the present.

Sheepy Wood, as figure 13.9 shows, has a fine woodland recession bank along its northern part, indicating the wood was once more extensive than at present. Documentary evidence confirms its present boundaries as unchanged since at least 1683.[42] The arrival of the Leicester to Nuneaton railway in the last century caused the removal of the wood's southern tip; otherwise the southern outline is that noted for the same seventeenth century date. The various remnant stretches of an ancient perimeter bank and ditch to the west and the absence of this feature elsewhere are also important. There are no archaeological features of interest within the wood except ponds, the dates of the creation of which are difficult to determine.

Burbage Wood also has sections of ancient wood banks which strongly indicate that the present wood has lost and gained sections prior to the seventeenth century. The archaeological evidence confirms this view. The wood's present outline has remained unchanged since at least 1683 with the exception of the thin strip of land bodering Smithy Lane.[43]

Both woods may be considered ancient woodlands but they have quite different origins. The most likely explanation for this situation appears to be that Sheepy Wood is an ancient undisturbed site and has functioned as a woodland with wood pasture over many centuries and that its once rich ancient woodland flora has suffered from adverse management at an unknown period or periods in the past. Burbage Wood, or substantial sections of it, has carried trees continuously for a very considerable time during which, with favourable management, a rich 'ancient woodland' flora has become established. Both Woods are clearly ancient, but Burbage is the younger of the two.

The origin of the name Sheepy is unknown and it is first recorded in the nineteenth century. Burbage Wood was known as 'The Spring Wood' in the eighteenth century and both woods were once associated with the manor's medieval park which existed for a short time in the late thirteenth and early fourteenth centuries.

At present Burbage Wood is dominated by a canopy of oak and ash, with many standards around 150 years of age. Field maple and hazel are the commonest species in the shrub layer, but there are many others present, as would be expected in a Boulder Clay wood. As at Breedon though, the clay is not as heavy as in East Leicestershire and there are species present which are more typical of acid soils, such as pendulous sedge, which is frequent. Sheepy Wood contains proportionally more oak than ash, and fewer species of base-rich soils. Otherwise the two woods are fairly similar.

Coppicing was re-introduced to the woods when Hinckley and Bosworth Borough Council took over the site in the 1980s, developing them as part of Burbage Common and Woods Country Park. Intense recreational pressure forced a

Figure 13.9

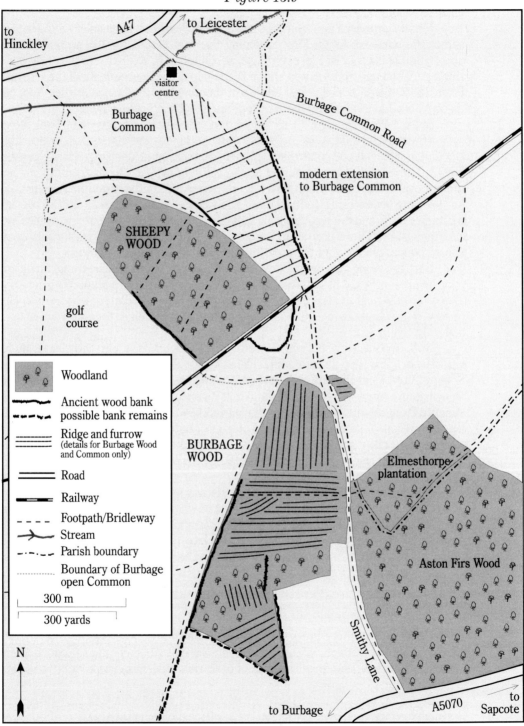

Legend:

- Woodland
- Ancient wood bank
- possible bank remains
- Ridge and furrow (details for Burbage Wood and Common only)
- Road
- Railway
- Footpath/Bridleway
- Stream
- Parish boundary
- Boundary of Burbage open Common

300 m

300 yards

N

SHEEPY WOOD and BURBAGE WOOD

compromise to accommodate visitors, and the paths and rides through the woods were laid with hard core. Apart from this some imaginative management work has ensured that this site is a valuable one for wildlife. The coppice panels produce wonderful displays of common spring flowers as well as rarer ones including greater butterfly-orchids. Natural regeneration in the plots is good, with rowan saplings abundant in places.

PRIOR'S COPPICE

*T*his woodland lies immediately to the south of Braunston village, Rutland, and extends over 70 acres of Boulder and Lias Clays. About half the area takes the form of a north-facing slope and this, with the wet and heavy nature of the soils, accounts very largely for its survival, unploughed and uncultivated, to the present. The major portion is situated in Leighfield parish, the remainder in the parish of Brooke.

From the point of view of its natural history, Prior's Coppice represents the best of the remaining few links with the Royal Forest of Leighfield. The wood is first mentioned by name in 1611 when it was described as containing about 36 acres.[44] It was referred to as forming part of the possessions of the dissolved Priory of Brooke and in the later sixteenth century was in the occupation of Andrew Noel.[45] The western section of the present wood was known as Swincliffe Coppice and was of unknown area. However, in 1564 this same section, under the name of Swynkecliffe was stated to contain 38 acres.[46] It contained oak and hazel with thorns and [crab] apple. Some of the oaks at that time were about 300 years old and there were many saleable as firewood.[47] At the same time the portion of the modern wood situated in Brooke parish was known as Brooke Wood. It seems likely therefore that the two sections comprising the present Prior's Coppice have occupied their present sites since at least the middle of the sixteenth century. The western portion was originally contained within the Royal Forest whilst the eastern one was not.

A study of local boundaries together with evidence from field surveys produces several other conclusions. First, it seems likely that both halves of the present wood are remnants of a much larger former woodland which was divided between the parishes of Leighfield and Brooke at a time long before the first surviving record of the mid sixteenth century. The Leighfield portion was retained by the monarch within the Royal Forest. The Brooke portion was probably taken from the Forest and became part of the property of Brooke Priory. This same area became known as Brooke Wood. It may also be part of the Domesday woodland listed under Oakham of which Brooke was an outlier. It was also probably associated with the hunting park of the priors of Brooke for which no medieval record appears to have survived.

A pattern of wood banks around and within the present Prior's Coppice suggests also that the two halves are remnants of the two portions of this supposed larger and earlier woodland. There is no ridge and furrow in either part of the modern wood, there are no known archaeological features and it seems likely that the soils have remained uncultivated for many centuries. Speed's Map of 1611 (Shown in Figure 7.8 on p.52) makes a recognisable representation of the wood's shape as compared with that on the early nineteenth century first edition of the One

Inch Ordnance Survey. We can presume that its boundaries as we now know them have changed only in minor ways, if at all, since the early seventeenth century.

Little is known about the Wood's early management although it has long been important as a fox covert. For many years following the cessation of coppicing, perhaps in the 1930s, only the Cottesmore Hunt carried out any management work. The Hunt needed to keep open some of the rides to facilitate access and were hampered by the very poor drainage. Their work resulted in the preservation of superb marshy grassland communities, containing showy species such as common spotted-orchid and ragged-robin.

The ancient division of Prior's Coppice into two separate areas became apparent once more during the Second World War when the Leighfield section was clear-felled. It was subsequently left to regenerate naturally and developed into derelict coppice. Many large oaks were formerly present but all that remain of these are large rotting stumps. Oak is now uncommon in this part of the wood, which is dominated by a multitude of ash poles, forty to fifty feet high, many growing from huge coppice stools up to twelve feet in diameter. The Brooke section of the Wood escaped clear-felling and is now developing into high forest. Oak is co-dominant with ash in the canopy with many specimens of the former species estimated at about 150 years old.

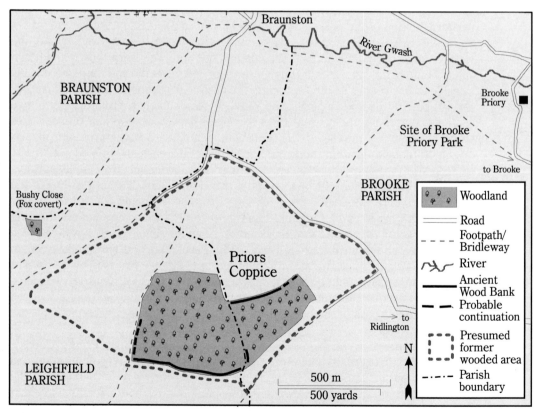

Figure 13.10   **PRIOR'S COPPICE**
in its historical context

The division into high forest and derelict coppice has produced noticeably different faunas and floras. Hole nesting birds, for example, are much more common in the high forest area, with a few species such as nuthatch and tree creeper almost totally confined to that area. Opportunities for nesting in the derelict coppice area are restricted due to scarcity of suitable nest holes, (see also figure 11.7 on p.95). Of the flowering plants, many are abundant in the area of derelict coppice, but rare where high forest occurs. Early purple-orchid and wood forget-me-not fall into this category. The explanation for this apparent preference in habitat probably lies in the fact that there is more light in the derelict coppice area where oak, a tree which casts heavy shade and the leaves of which form a deep leaf litter, is rare.

Prior's Coppice is typical of, although very much richer than, many other woods of high East Leicestershire. In particular the abundance of wood forget-me-not forms blue sheets in the spring. Other attractive woodland plants which help make the Wood a memorable place at that time include wood anemone, red campion, bluebell, wood sorrel and primrose. Rarer species such as herb Paris, violet helleborine and greater butterfly-orchid can also be found.

In 1987 Prior's Coppice was purchased by the Leicestershire and Rutland Trust for Nature Conservation, and it is now managed as a nature reserve. Coppicing has been re-introduced, and the effects of this are being monitored. The reserve is open to the public, who are encouraged to visit what is one of the finest woodland nature reserves in the Midlands. The maintenance of the integrity of the site is paramount, however, and with the continuing decline in the nature conservation value of our woodlands, Prior's Coppice is likely to become even more important.

SKEFFINGTON and TILTON WOODS

Skeffington Woods (about 70 acres) and Tilton Wood (about 25 acres) lie alongside the Eye Brook, with a south-west aspect in a most attractive area of countryside. The geology of the site is complex, consisting of Lias clays and Marlstone bed-rock, overlain in places with glacial deposits of Boulder clay and sand and gravel. Small stream valleys lead down to the brook, and there is some marshy ground. It is quite clear that both sites were once part of the same woodland complex but they appear to have undergone different forms of development over the last few centuries.

Domesday Book records 50 acres of wood for Skeffington but there are no other records of woodland until the thirteenth century, when the Abbey of Croxton held a meadow 'below Randulfwode'.[48] The same abbey also held a wood called 'Endrisland', and along with the Priory of Launde, held various lands in the parish with common of pasture on the moorland to the south-east of the present wood.[49] By the close of the sixteenth century there were at least 140 acres of woodland, with a possible further 60 acres to the south of the Eye Brook.[50] Nichols notes that in 1665 the plague raged at Skeffington such that the villagers fled to the woods and lived in temporary huts until it was over.[51]

At the start of the nineteenth century the pattern of woodlands and the names by which they are known had changed. In 1800 Great Wood contained 19 acres, Eagland Wood c.10 acres, Hoothill Wood c.15 acres, Many Bush Wood (now Browns Wood) c.9 acres and Brome Wood c.25 acres.[52] This last name originated some time

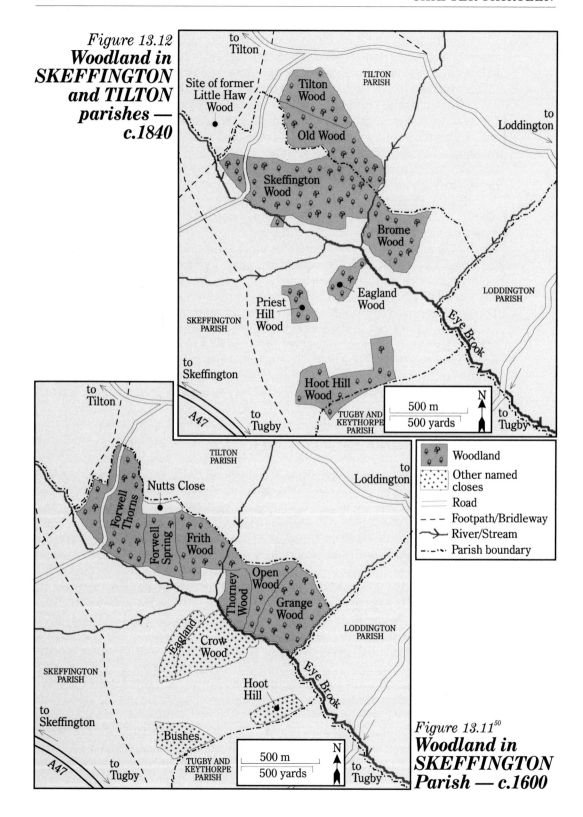

Figure 13.12
Woodland in SKEFFINGTON and TILTON parishes — c.1840

Figure 13.11[50]
Woodland in SKEFFINGTON Parish — c.1600

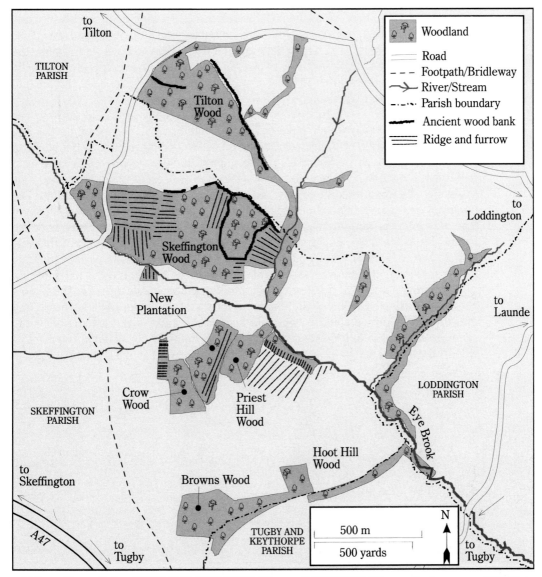

Woodland in SKEFFINGTON and TILTON parishes — 1990

Figure 13.13

in the sixteenth century when William Brome received part of the manor of Skeffington. Subsequent changes meant that by 1990 the area of woodland had decreased very slightly.

There are few documentary references to the history of Tilton Wood. Domesday Book records 5 acres for that part of the parish that was an outlier of Rothley Manor. For the rest of Tilton no woodland is listed. In 1461 Everard Digby had 30 acres of wood in Tilton,[53] and in 1644 the value of the timber and underwood of the manor was £3,816.13s.4d.[54] This figure included income derived from woods, now lost, called Short Wood and Hallwood. In 1840, judging from place name evidence, Old Wood formed the southern boundary of Tilton Wood and was close upon the parish boundary with Skeffington. Little Hallwood also lay against the parish boundary at the western tip of Skeffington Wood. The disappearance of Old Wood some time during the fifty or so years following 1835 produced the present boundaries of Tilton Wood.

Archaeological evidence from both air photography and field survey also suggests that the two woods have developed differently. Tilton Wood on the one hand is the remnant of a much larger medieval wood, the southern boundary of which adjoined the parish boundary as late as 1840. Field survey reveals that at least half this wood stood on ridge and furrow. The area at present under trees offers no evidence of having undergone any disturbance, at least not by the plough. The boundary bank along its northern edge is of massive proportions and clearly ancient. The only internal bank of unknown origin and purpose, is also old. The site of the former Little Haw Wood also shows ridge and furrow but whether or not this was formed before or after the Wood's appearance is not known. The parish is largely fertile and much of it shows the signs of continuous cultivation over a long period.

Approximately half the present Skeffington Wood stands on ridge and furrow showing clearly the signs of the changing medieval landscape. Furthermore, the entire wood is surrounded by ridge and furrow and most of the parish shows the same feature, some of it decidedly complex. The boundary bank along the present wood's northern edge is comparable in age and size with that at Tilton and marks an

Figure 13.14
Skeffington and Tilton Woods seen from the south-east.

Figure 13.15
Skeffington Wood after coppicing in 1981.

early division of woodland in the two manors, apparently along the line of the parish boundary, or at least part of it. Alone, the field known as Nutts Close, which also shows signs of ridge and furrow, has remained treeless for at least four centuries. Part of the western portion of the site of the former Brome's Wood also shows signs of earlier ploughing but the rest, including the sites of the former Open Wood and Grange Wood, although surrounded by ridge and furrow, show no disturbance. A curious feature is a small woodland, presumably the site of the former Frith Wood, fossilized at the eastern end of the modern wood.

Of the remaining woodlands, only the present Crow Wood, Brown's Wood and Hoot Hill Wood appear to be on undisturbed sites. The rest all stand on ridge and furrow.

Both Skeffington and Tilton Woods are ash woods, but hazel, oak and field maple are all frequent too. Alder occurs in the stream valleys and there are many other trees and shrubs, with ivy locally frequent as a climber and in the field layer where the soils have been disturbed. Honeysuckle is frequent as a climber in the shrub layer throughout, creating tangled thickets that are characteristic of the rich ash woods of East Leicestershire.

Large, scattered stools of ash in particular testify to the past management history of the woods, but in recent decades modern forestry practices have been employed, and parts have been clear-felled and planted first with conifers, and later with broadleaves. Other areas have been thinned and ash stools managed to encourage the development of a high forest structure.

The varied geology, including calcareous clays, has given rise to an extremely diverse flora. Bluebell, wood anemone, dog's mercury and woodruff are all abundant, while the eastern end of Skeffington Wood contains huge carpets of ramsons. Many plants present are associated with ancient woodland in the county, especially the thin-spiked wood-sedge, the lovely violet helleborine, and herb paris. A stand of common reed and hemp-agrimony in a wet peaty area of Skeffington Wood is a unique feature in East Leicestershire woodlands.

SOUTHWOOD

*S*outhwood lies two miles north-north-west of Ashby-de-la-Zouch and extends over some 147 acres. Until recently it adjoined the county boundary but in 1991 was transferred in its entirety to the Derbyshire parish of Smisby. The following account does not take note of this change.

The wood lies entirely on the coal measures of north-west Leicestershire and South Derbyshire. These rocks can produce both light and heavy soils and those in

Figure 13.16 Southwood seen from the north-west.

Southwood are generally light, free-draining and acid in nature with some clayey areas where drainage is poor. The overall topography is flat or gently undulating except in the western section (Bryan's Coppice) and where streams and drainage channels have cut ravines from west to east.

Accounting for the history of Southwood presents particular problems since documentary references are scarce and physical evidence from the landscape is varied, fragmented and difficult to interpret. As with many other large Leicestershire woodlands the present wood is merely the latest stage in a slow evolution over many centuries. The development can best be appreciated when seen against that of other areas of woodland and heath, which have existed locally at the hand of man on impoverished soils for a long period. Such a view must also include the intermittent operations of small-scale coalmining over several centuries, common grazing on an extensive scale and the development and decline of at least two medieval deer parks.

From the record of Domesday Book (1086) it is clear that the area of South Derbyshire known today as Calke, together with the southern part of Ticknall parish and the eastern part of Smisby, was occupied by large stretches of open, unfenced and rough grassland with considerable extents of wood pasture and patches of woodland hedged or fenced against cattle. Place name and other evidence suggests that much of the open grazing was heathland which since Saxon times had been used on an inter-communal basis by the inhabitants of the respective manors.

In the mid twelfth century one of the named woodlands was 'Southwode', which was the property of Ranulf, earl of Chester (died 1153), who gave the canons of Calke leave to take wood to make charcoal.[55] The wood was located immediately north of the county boundary and extended an unknown distance southwards, perhaps into Leicestershire. The same 'Southwode' is mentioned as woodland in 1260[56] and again in 1282.[57] In 1537 John Prest was licensed to take wood from 'all the woods and underwoods called southwode'.[58] Fifty years later in 1585 the earl of Huntingdon's manor of Ashby contained 'a wood ground called Southwood', and three parks.[59] In 1635 John Archer was occupying 'a dwelling house and cottage' with closes of 'pasture ground' which had been created from the wood.[60] (This was probably the site of the modest dwelling later known as Ashby Southwood Farm, lying to the east of the wood). It seems that by this time the Derbyshire part of 'Southwood' had been cleared of much of its tree cover and had been at least partly inclosed. Further inclosures were being made in 1775[61] and in 1820 the whole of the common was inclosed.[62]

The creation of the two medieval deer parks also influenced the development of the Leicestershire portion of Southwood. On the south-west edge, including the present Bryan's Coppice, lay Smisby Park, known only from one reference of 1328 when it contained wood and provided pannage for pigs.[63] Nearby in Leicestershire, and to the south-east of the present wood, was the site of the park of Ashby, first noted in 1337, which also contained wood.[64] Both parks were short-lived, the former being turned over to agriculture and the latter being re-sited elsewhere.

The absence of ridge and furrow from all parts of Southwood suggests no section of the wooded area has ever been ploughed. Adjoining fields show signs of early cultivation. The main archaeological features of importance are the remains of ancient coalmines which are scattered thickly about the northern half of the wood.

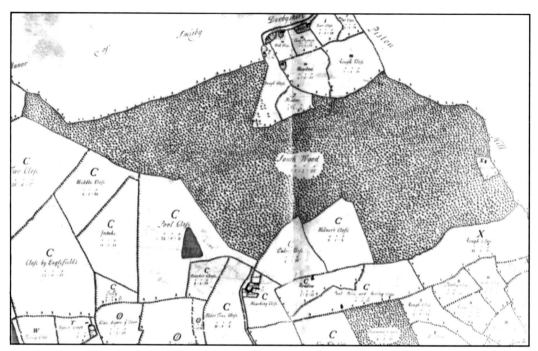

Figure 13.17 Southwood in 1735.

(See figure 13.18). It is clear that groups of mines were created at different times. One group on the northern edge of the wood exploited the coal seams located close to the surface. Such pits probably represent simple efforts at extraction from the thirteenth century or earlier. Pits of the eastern edge and others towards the centre of the wood are altogether larger and mark places where the more deeply-lying seams have been tackled, probably no later than 1600. Dating such features with accuracy is difficult since as late as the early eighteenth century coal delphs were still being worked in Southwood.[65] At that time the wood lay open to Pistern Hills Common and was used for grazing by the earl of Huntingdon's tenants. The northern edge of the wood, still the boundary, was finally fenced, and a strip of land towards the valley bottom was left to make some recompense for the lost grazing.

The complex pattern of fragments of internal banks and ditches contributes only a little to our ideas of the Wood's development. The absence of a boundary bank along the north-east perimeter can be accounted for by the known history of common grazing and the great likelihood that the early mining was carried out on heathland rather than in woodland. At the north-east tip an area of early clearance and inclosure from either woodland or heathland, is indicated by the pattern of small fields of irregular shape. Overall, the evidence points to the southern and western parts of the wood being least disturbed. To the north and east of the hamlet known as Wicket Nook, which probably arose from a casual settlement on Smisby Common, it is evident that two large areas were taken from the Wood at an early date, leaving one section of the original boundary bank isolated under a hedge line. The present bank along the edge of the wood which runs south-south-east from Wicket Nook may well be a remnant of the pale bank of Smisby deer park.

Figure 13.18

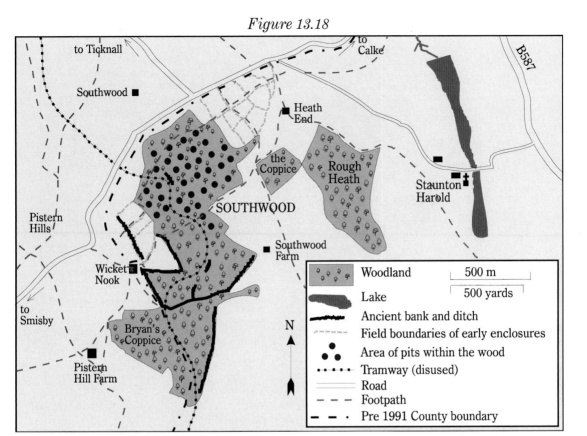

SOUTHWOOD near Ashby–de–la–Zouch

Between 1802 and 1915 a horse drawn tramway taking lime from Ticknall limeworks to the railway at Ashby operated through the wood. The construction involved the creation of considerable lengths of cuttings and embankments. The ballast for securing the simple track was largely alkaline in nature which produced a strong contrast to the soils of the area and added considerably to the arrival of new plant species.

Southwood was acquired by the Harpur Crewe estates about the turn of the 20th century. Judging from the complex network of drainage channels and other earthworks, management of the wood was once quite vigorous. In recent years there has been little money spent on upkeep and maintenance. To the west of the line of the tramway clear felling took place after World War II and conifers were introduced. Selective felling also seems to have come to a halt and the chief influences on the wildlife are the grazing by deer, shooting by a syndicate and the occasional visit from the foxhunt. In 1985 Southwood passed to the National Trust as part of the Calke Abbey Estate.

The predominance of poor, acid soil has meant the flora of the wood is not rich. However, this wood is a large one in the local context and contains some superb stands of mature oak, with many specimens around 200 years of age. Both our native oaks are present, the rarer sessile oak occurring on the better drained soils. Few

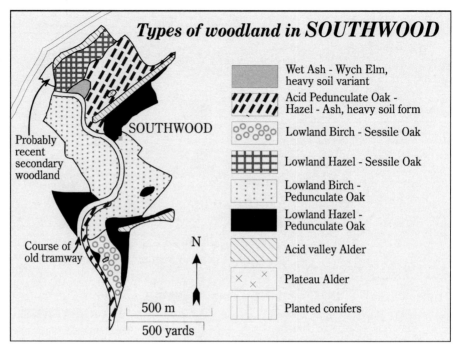

Figure 13.19

other trees are constituents of the canopy, although ash, alder and elm all form local associations. The result is the intricate mosaic of vegetation types shown in the map above. Several very large beech trees, presumably deliberately planted here and estimated to be around 300 years old, are also present.

The shrub layer is sparse, with hazel and holly the main species present. One hazel stool measuring nearly 3 feet across, is actually growing in a partially filled in mineshaft, indicating that the pit is very old. A few of the larger hollies have been grazed by deer, and horizontal browse lines can now be clearly seen about six feet above the ground.

Throughout most of Southwood the ground flora is noticeably species-poor. Brambles, bracken and creeping soft-grass are abundant, and bluebells locally so. Plants characteristic of acid soils like wood sage, hairy wood-rush and broad buckler-fern can be found, but it is only in the stream valleys and along the mineral line that the variety of species increases. Along the streams opposite-leaved golden-saxifrage and the locally rare thin-spiked wood-sedge occur, the latter being one of the best indicators of ancient woodland in Leicestershire. Perhaps it persisted in tree-lined stream valleys even when most of what is now Southwood was heathland. On the mineral line are many plants that are not found elsewhere in the wood, such as wild basil and woodruff.

The fauna of Southwood does not appear to have been studied in detail, but there is sufficient information available to make it clear that the wood is an important site for some groups. A rich dead-wood fauna is present, associated with large quantities of standing and lying dead wood. Few other sites in the area can compare in this respect.

Chapter Fourteen
Modern Woodland Management

*T*he changes in the development and uses over the centuries of woodland in Leicestershire, from its natural state to the semi-natural condition in which we see most of it today, have been a primary theme of this book. Generations of local people have managed, in various ways, their local woodlands for a variety of reasons: personal, communal, financial and aesthetic. Seldom has encouraging the richness of the wildlife been considered a primary purpose. Now, however, more and more effort is being made in this direction and management is increasingly practising sound ecological principles.

The floras of ancient woodlands in particular can be influenced by different management regimes, some of which have been developed in Leicestershire and Rutland. Coppicing, for example, often produces superb shows of flowers in the first few years of the cycle. At Prior's Coppice, re-introduction of coppicing in the late 1980's resulted in carpets of wood anemones, together with wood forget-me-nots and primroses, appearing in the spring. Other plants which have responded to this form of traditional management at this site include soft rush, common spotted-orchid, hairy St. John's-wort, tufted hair-grass and red campion.

Figure 14.1 A ride in Skeffington Wood.

Figure 14.2
Prior's Coppice, following the re-introduction of medieval-type coppice management. Wood anemones grew in abundance when the canopy was opened up.

When an area in Great Merrible Wood was coppiced, in 1983, a large colony of herb paris developed. Bluebells also did well in the coppice plots in this wood. Unfortunately though, conditions also suited common nettle, cleavers, elder, blackthorn and lesser burdock and these vigorous species out-competed the more attractive woodland herbs. The reinstatement of coppicing at Burbage and Sheepy Woods also produced good displays of wood anemones, as well as wood millet and water avens.

No woodland plants in the county actually seem to depend on coppicing for their existence, however. Although coppicing did not take place in the counties for more than 40 years, there is no evidence to show that the extinction of any species occurred. Species such as wood anemone were doing well at Prior's Coppice even before coppicing was re-introduced.

It is the loss of woodland rides which has perhaps had a more profound effect on plants in woods, reducing the numbers of species present at sites such as Oakley Wood, where the rides are now narrow and heavily shaded. Woodland edge species such as hairy St. John's-wort have suffered, in addition to non-woodland plants such as ragged-robin. The actual woodland edges too, it should be noted, are probably not now as suitable for some plants as a result of recent agricultural intensification, including the drift from herbicide spraying. Many woodland invertebrates have also been affected in some way.

A few woodland plants appear to be adversely affected by coppicing. The population of hard shield-fern at Prior's Coppice, for example, has increased markedly in the last 25 years in the absence of coppicing. This wood is also rich in other fern species, which may have benefited similarly. After the first coppice plot was cut in the winter of 1987/88 many ferns came up in the following spring, but soon withered away in the unfavourable conditions in which they then found themselves. Opposite-leaved golden-saxifrage and the thin-spiked wood-sedge are two other species which declined markedly following coppicing at that site.

Not surprisingly, the planting of conifers has a detrimental effect on the flora of ancient woodlands, though some species can hang on in reduced numbers. Where pockets of the original semi-natural woodland are left, as at Wardley Wood, there is reasonable hope that removal of the conifers will result in some recovery of the flora. Much depends on which trees are then re-planted. Foresters may well prefer to plant mainly oaks, but too many oaks will inhibit the ground flora through heavy shade and deep leaf-litter. It is probable that only the woods on the more acid soils of Charnwood and the Coalfield of north-west Leicestershire, together with central Rutland had large numbers of oaks naturally present in them. Oak regeneration is not strong outside these areas, but natural regeneration should be employed wherever possible in woods, since this will lead to a more natural mix and spacing of trees.

In some woods the semi-natural woodland is returning. At Owston for example, where the soil is heavy clay, compartments planted with conifers have not done well and the conifers have now been over-topped by ash and alder.

Figure 14.3 Hard shield fern – a species which benefits from the deeper shade which develops following the abandonment of coppicing. It is seen here growing amongst wood anemones and dog's mercury.

Chapter Fifteen
Evaluating Woodlands

Various methods have been tried to evaluate woodlands on the basis of the richness of their flora and fauna.[1] These methods have mainly relied on point scoring systems, and all have suffered from attempts to compare different site features. How, for example, do we value wide grassy rides against the presence of old trees?

In Leicestershire and Rutland a system originally developed for use in Norfolk has been employed.[2] It involves the compilation of a 'league table', through a *flora score*. This score is the number of species of woodland plants known to have been recorded from a particular site, excluding trees and shrubs. A table of Leicestershire and Rutland woods has been drawn up, and the top ten are shown in figure 15.2.

The flora score has been used as the basis of the evaluation, but the list has been fine-tuned to take into account of the present state of the wood. It may be affected by sycamore invasion for example; or have a poor structure; neglected rides; or not be as species-rich as it once was. Cloud Wood drops down the list, for example, because of the adverse effects of the quarrying activities.

Of the ten woods in figure 15.2, Swithland, Owston and Burley stand clear as the top three. These really are very fine woodlands, and could rate highly in any comparison with woods from elsewhere in Britain. To illustrate this, flora scores have been calculated for three well known Cambridgeshire woods of exceptional

*Figure 15.1
An ancient
perimeter wood
bank at Oakley
Wood.*

nature conservation value, and are shown in figure 15.3 alongside the top three from Leicestershire and Rutland.[3]

It is interesting to note that Buddon Wood had a remarkable score of 151, nearly as high as that of Bedford Purlieus, which is probably the richest woodland in Britain. Unfortunately, little of Buddon Wood; remains, it having been largely destroyed by quarrying activities, and many of the plants are no longer present. One wonders how long it will be before other similarly important sites are quarried away, or otherwise destroyed.

The information gathered recently has also been used to determine which Leicestershire and Rutland woodlands are the most valuable for nature conservation purposes.

Figure 15.2

Leicestershire and Rutland woods in order of importance for nature conservation

Wood	Flora score	Some evaluation factors
1. Swithland Wood	147	Fine high forest structure; 9 stand types; very species-rich; well recorded history; grassland and quarries within site; sycamore and public use problems.
2. Owston Woods	132	Very large site; contains largest continuous area of semi-natural woodland in Leicestershire; very species-rich; 7 stand types; good rides; well recorded; giant coppice stools.
3. Burley Wood	125	The modern county's largest ancient woodland; fine high forest structure; old trees; well recorded; good rides; important lichen flora; sycamore.
4. Prior's Coppice	114	Species-rich; good rides; well recorded; good structure; nature reserve.
5. Grace Dieu Wood	112	Fine wet alder woodland; 7 stand types; species-rich; good stream; sycamore and rhododendron invasion.
6. Launde Big Wood	108	Species-rich; good rides; large semi-natural site.
7. Skeffington Wood	103	Species-rich; 6 stand types; varied structure; good rides.
8. Pasture & Asplin Woods	95/ 91	Can be treated as one site; good structure; species-rich; grassland within site.
9. Cloud Wood	106	Species-rich; reduced in size by quarrying; rides damaged by tipping of spoil; nature reserve.
10. Loddington Reddish	93	Large semi-natural site; species-rich.

Flora score = number of woodland plants (excluding trees and shrubs) recorded at the site. Buddon Wood had the highest flora score of all woods in the two counties, with 151.

| Wood | Size | | Flora |
	ha	acres	score
Bedford Purlieus, Cambs	218	539	158
Monk's Wood, Cambs	157	388	143
Hayley Wood, Cambs	49	121	110
Swithland Wood	70	173	147
Owston Wood	146	360	132
Burley Wood	156	385	125

Figure 15.3
Comparison of the top three woodlands in Leicestershire and Rutland with three Cambridgeshire woodlands.

Figure 15.4

Discovering Woodlands

The first visit to a wood can sometimes reveal a great deal. What species of trees and shrubs are present? Is there a mixture or is the wood devoted to growing only say oak or ash? Are the trees in single-species stands or are there mixed groupings? The size of the trees will suggest their ages. Tiny saplings will indicate natural regeneration. Stands of one age show serious efforts at timber production. Ancient standards may reflect an intention long ago forgotten. Are pollards and coppice, when present, showing signs of being harvested?

The management of a wood, now and in the past, may be told in other ways. Well maintained tracks, fire breaks and open rides; trimmed trunks and branches; sawdust, chippings, newly-cut logs and the signs of bonfires all indicate that a wood is being actively managed. Perimeter gates may be maintained to allow the hunt access and spent cartridges indicate visits by shooting parties. Woodlands in the hands of institutions, such as the local council, will attract more public access than those in private hands. Stiles and gates will be present; tracks will be well sign posted; muddy places will show the prints of dogs as well as those of their owners and litter may be present.

A wood's management, or lack of it, has a profound effect on the flora and fauna. The herb flora is of special interest in this respect as is shown in Chapter 11. The presence of certain lichen species growing on the trunks and branches may be an indication of the antiquity of the site. The invertebrate animals too, especially the beetles, spiders and micro moths may be of considerable interest. Some species are very demanding in their ecological requirements and are little able to withstand change. They show little ability to spread to surrounding habitats, however suitable they seem to us.

Figure 15.5

Woodland Archaeology

The presence of a massive bank with ditch along the perimeter of a wood is a certain sign that at least part of the site is one of ancient woodland. Oakley Wood (Shepshed), shown in figure 15.1, Pasture Wood (Breedon) and Tilton Wood have particularly fine ancient wood banks. Such banks support ancient pollards and coppice stools, themselves of great age. Burleigh Wood (Loughborough) has a bank on the inside, rather than the outside, which doubles as part of a hunting park boundary pale. Woodland edges which follow irregular or sinuous lines, bending to avoid long-lost features and making no sense on the modern landscape, contrast sharply with the straight edges and sharp corners of the more recent planner.

The internal archaeological features are no less important. If ridge and furrow is present it can usually be detected, especially along unimproved woodland tracks. Clearly, such land was at one time under the plough and cleared of trees. Ambion Wood (Sutton Cheney) is entirely on the ridge and furrow of the field system of the deserted village of Ambion. Much of this wood occupies the site of the march of Henry Tudor which figures in accounts of the Battle of Bosworth (1485).

In places a wood may turn up archaeological sites of other kinds. Former settlements indicated by pottery scatters; the subterranean footings of buildings; remains of former rail or tramways and the signs of early industry such as iron-working and charcoal burning, may remain to be found. Not all will suggest woodland destruction or decay, since early industry supported woodland rather than destroyed it. On a modern well-cultivated landscape woodland areas are often the best retainers of fragments of earlier human activity. The wood known as Wingfield Spinney at Nevill Holt, for example, preserves an entire moated site.

The pattern of a wood's internal banks and ditches may often reflect no more than serious efforts at drainage and maintenance. Alternatively such banks may indicate ownership of different areas by various persons at some distant age, remaining long after their original usefulness. Division of a manor's woodland between two or more heiresses was not unusual. Occasionally, internal divisions will be shown by a line of boundary stones bearing the marks of the adjacent owners. In Swithland Wood 18th century markers separate the woods of the Danvers family from those of the Greys, earls of Stamford.

Figure 15.6

Woodland Names

A wood's name may reveal much about its history. The wood may share the name of the parish (a possible link with antiquity) or bear the name of an early, possibly much earlier, owner. King's Wood (Leicester Forest) and Prior's Coppice (Braunston in Rutland) indicate former royal and monastic woodlands respectively. Sandyhurst Wood (Braunstone, Leicester) and Billesdon Coplow tell something of the physical nature of the site. Le Ker (Frisby) is an alder carr (boggy ground); le Soullowes (Kirby Muxloe), le Willows (Nailstone) and Loddington Reddish – the reedy place – have much the same message. Conegree Wood (Croxton Kerrial) is one of many local sites of former rabbit warrens and Mill Hill Spinney (Little Dalby) indicates another lost feature.

The familiar terms 'coppice' and 'spinney' are both indicators of the ancient practice of coppicing. 'Swineland' at Burton Lazars and Cold Newton refers to woodlands used for feeding pigs, whilst 'Pasture Wood' at Breedon extends the provision to other domestic stock. In more recent times the names 'gorse', 'furze' and 'covert' were adopted by 18th century local worthies who created small isolated woods for the purpose of foxhunting.

Sometimes a wood's name refers to another feature of the local landscape. 'Outwoods', in its four known Leicestershire examples, refers to sites adjacent to medieval deer parks. An 'Old Park Wood' may very well be on such a site. The clearance of woodland has left a rich legacy of woodland names such as 'Stocking Wood' and 'Breach Wood'.

Chapter Sixteen

The Future of Leicestershire and Rutland Woodland

Since Neolithic times both Leicestershire and Rutland have been poorly wooded compared with most other parts of lowland England. Yet it is because woodland has been a vital resource to the survival of generations of local people that the little we have always had has proved such an enduring feature of our landscape. This book has attempted to outline the course of the evolution of our woodland heritage and to comment on some aspects of the wildlife which it supports.

For much of the period before the Industrial Revolution demand, both in nature and volume, for woodland products developed very little. Management systems in particular changed only slowly. The long continuum accounted for not only a heritage of rich wildlife but also one in social, economic and cultural terms. Now, in the late 20th century, change in the countryside, commenced by the Industrial Revolution and accelerated by the Electronic Revolution, proceeds at breakneck speed. Planning, production, supply, transport and finance, once local considerations, are now usually matters of national or international concern. The survival of our woodlands must inevitably depend on the value which the present and future generations place upon them. It is therefore important to identify the different views of woodland, the parties in control of decision-making and the interests they serve.

In the first place there are the timber growers whose actions represent investment made against predicted returns. Their schemes, although helped by grant incentives and tax advantages, are subject to many restrictions and demands aimed at promoting various and changing government policies. In the short term, profits from timber can be realised after between 20 and 40 years where conifers are involved. The growing of broad leaf species usually involves much longer-term considerations since an oak, for example, will produce its best return when felled between 80 and 100 years old. The growing of coppice for wood rather than timber, whilst on the increase in our two counties, is still considered an uncertain means of investing capital even in the short term since markets are so uncertain.

A major consideration in the managing of local woodland, one supported by long tradition, is that of the role of the sportsmen. The rich legacy of woodlands founded and fostered over the years by the fox hunts has always preserved much more than fox populations. In some areas of the two counties these modest woodlands are the only areas of wildlife which have survived the virtual sterilization of the landscape by modern farming practices. Moreover, some patches of more ancient woodland probably owe their survival through difficult times to the activity of sportsmen. Already wealthy foreign shooting parties from Europe visit the woodlands of local estates for the sport they provide. Whatever one's view of field sports there is no doubting the considerable contribution of sportsmen to the wooded aspects of our present landscape.

The close relationship between agriculture and woodland has been of fundamental importance since land has been constantly taken in and out of husbandry over the centuries. Indeed on the local scene there have been only two periods over the last 1,000 years, the 12th century and the second half of the 16th century, when the loss of woodland, at the hands of the farmer, greatly exceeded the gain from various sources. Since the second World War agricultural policies have meant that fields have been enlarged by the removal of hedges, with the result that woods have become isolated. The use of chemical sprays has weakened or extinguished other links between woodland and field and, in the worst cases, has meant the direct destruction of woodland wildlife. Many farmers have felt there was nothing to be gained in spending money on their woodlands and essential management has thus been neglected.

In the late 20th century the claims of the conservationist for a voice in the management of woodlands, both public and private, are as strong as most. The conservation interest is no longer regarded as a quaint optional 'extra' in planning matters. Whereas some woodlands, by reason of their size and position may well be able to accommodate a variety of interests, other woodlands may not. The overriding value of such places is clearly in the richness of their living communities which can be so easily devalued and destroyed.

A parallel case can be made by another branch of what is sometimes seen as the 'heritage lobby'. There is no doubt that some of our finest woodlands are essentially the work of earlier generations of landscape gardeners. Burley-on-the-Hill owes its present exquisite form to the activities of successive wealthy and expressive owners and their employees, among them the celebrated Humphry Repton (1752-1818). The value of preserving such landscapes in a countryside which is losing much of its interest is becoming increasingly recognised.

The growing importance of woodlands for amenity purposes has already been noted. The demands are both numerous and diverse and in many cases are conflicting. On the one hand there are the wanderers whose only wish is for solitude, peace and quiet and a desire to 'get away from it all'. Their visits together with those of the majority of weekend walkers may disturb or damage the wood hardly at all. Dog walkers tend to be more frequent visitors and uncontrolled animals can disturb and destroy wildlife. The activities of campers and picnickers, too, have a marked effect on the flora and fauna especially where waste disposal and the risk of fire are involved. Finally, there are the war-gamers and orienteerers whose activities, by their very nature, are often damaging to historical features and finely-balanced wildlife communities.

We have already described a variety of pressures, largely originating in the 19th and 20th centuries, which show no sign of abating and which form major threats to woodland in the future. In particular, the growth of the mining and quarrying industries continue to pose serious problems to woodland on the soils over old hard rocks or on those of the coal measures where much remaining woodland is found. Closely linked with granite production is the current road programme, especially the development of new motorways and major trunk roads and the widening of existing ones. It would be difficult to find a county which has been more centrally concerned

Figure 16.1
Campers at Cathill Wood, Charnwood Forest. The use of ancient woodland
sites for recreational purposes has increased greatly in recent years.

with both issues than Leicestershire. It is to be welcomed that many such development sites have received some 'landscaping', but even the most carefully planned and managed motorway embankment or cutting is no substitute for a woodland community, the diversity, interest and value of which is the result of centuries of evolution.

The designation in the 1970s of Leicestershire and Rutland as 'growth' counties has resulted in a great expansion of the urban area. Whatever the planners may or may not care to admit it is not difficult to visualize the day when Derby will effectively become joined to Nottingham along the Trent Valley and A52, when Leicester will be joined to Loughborough along the Soar Valley and A6, and Hinckley joined to Earl Shilton along the A47. Moreover, there are several applications pending for new 'villages' in parts of Leicestershire. One wonders about the possibility of a proposal for one such village in the 'empty' uplands of East Leicestershire. But it is not just the bricks and mortar which degrade or destroy woodland. The arrival of an urban fringe usually creates a 'twilight' zone which promotes decline, decay and abandonment.

Clearly, a large proportion of the responsibility for the future of woodland lies in the hands of the planners, both those who plan and manage individual groups of woodland and those who operate on a wider scale. Of the first group are various statutory bodies such as the Forestry Commission (who currently manage Owston Wood, Launde Woods and Pickworth Great Wood for example) and English Nature.

Other voluntary bodies are the Leicestershire and Rutland Trust for Nature Conservation, who manage a variety of woods including Cloud Wood and Prior's Coppice, the National Trust (Southwood) and the Woodland Trust (Martinshaw and Polebrook Woods). Each of these groups manages its woodlands to particular ends. Without such purposeful effort, made possible by finances from various sources, the woodland may in some cases revert to less interesting, less diverse, less beautiful and less valuable forms of vegetation. Its long term future would thus be placed in serious jeopardy.

The second group of planners see woodland as just one aspect of the total landscape, rural and urban. The role of woodland in the lives of most people has changed and many of these officials have been slow to recognise the facts or have been constrained from action. In the late 20th century, the reasoning goes, any particular wood is no longer the exclusive preserve of its owner or the local people; for particular reasons it 'belongs' to the whole district or even the region. Its importance may extend to national or even international level with its prospects for the future, and finance to secure the same, coming from abroad.

In Leicestershire and Rutland about 130 woodlands are said to be ancient, i.e. they are growing on sites which have been continuously wooded since at least the year 1600AD. These now receive some protection from the present Leicestershire County Council Replacement Structure Plan and some are managed with grants from the Forestry Commission. Of these sites a total of 40 have statutory protection, in all or part, as SSSIs under the 1981 Wildlife and Countryside Act. Two such: Leighfield Forest (a group of East Leicestershire and West Rutland woodlands) and

Figure 16.2

Leicestershire and Rutland Woodlands which are wholly or in part Sites of Special Scientific Interest (SSSIs).

(Those which are managed as Nature Reserves are marked NR.)

Allexton Wood	East Wood	Pasture Wood
Armley Wood	Grace Dieu Wood	Pickworth Great Wood
Asplin Wood	Great Merrible Wood (NR)	(NR)
Aston Firs (part NR)	Groby Pool Wood	Prior's Coppice (NR)
Bardon Hill Wood	Hambleton Wood	Rushpit Wood
Barnsdale Wood	Holyoaks Wood	Sheet Hedges Wood
Benscliffe Wood	Hoothill Wood	Skeffington Wood
Bolt Wood	Launde Big Wood	Spring Wood (part NR)
Brazil Wood (NR)	Loddington Reddish	Stoneywell Wood
Brown's Wood	Newall Wood	Swithland Wood
Buddon Wood	Oakley Wood	Tilton Wood
Burbage Wood (NR)	Outwoods	Tugby Bushes
Burley Wood	Owston Woods	Tugby Wood
Cloud Wood (NR)	Park Wood	

Swithland Wood are regarded as two of Britain's key conservation sites.[1] However, legislation has not resulted in the positive management of many sites, but rather has slowed down the rate of their destruction from neglect, their 'development' towards other ends, and even from grubbing up.

The important point is whether or not woodland conservation as seen by the planners at the higher levels should be given equal status with the other demands on the landscape so vigorously promoted by well-organised and well-financed pressure groups. At present it is much easier to demonstrate the 'need' for a new east-west road through rural east Leicestershire (perhaps to serve a proposed new village) than the 'need' on the grounds of cost, for re-routing the road to prevent the destruction of, say, Launde Big Wood. Likewise in another context, the raising of funds from both private and public sources to save an historic house from decay or destruction would present less difficulty than to save an ancient woodland, even though the latter could be shown to be of similar significance, much greater age, and equally a creation of man.

In the end it is a matter of assessing our 'needs' as opposed to 'demands', of recognising long-term and short-term gain and loss, and of determining sources of public and private income. Who shall own, use and manage our woodlands and to what ends? Who will pay for the work and what will their rewards be? At present Leicestershire and Rutland still have a rich woodland heritage. Its conservation for future generations is in the hands of the present one.

Appendix One

Access to the Woods

While the majority of Leicestershire woods are privately owned and therefore difficult to access, some of the most interesting are open to the public. Moreover, many others can be viewed from public footpaths or roads. A selection of those woods which best show the features described in this book, or simply allow enjoyment of woodlands, is listed below. In addition to the names of the woods, the parish, district and grid reference are given, as are the Ordnance Survey 1:50000 map numbers. Further information on some of the woods can be found in *A Guide to Nature Reserves in Leicestershire and Rutland,* available from the Leicestershire and Rutland Trust for Nature Conservation (LRTNC), 1 West Street, Leicester, LE1 6UU. Details of Trust membership are also available from this address.

Barkby Holt, Barkby

(Charnwood Borough) - SK 672096   O.S. Map No. 141

This is a large, secondary woodland/plantation, which nicely exhibits many of the characteristics of such sites, e.g. pronounced ridge and furrow, straight edges to the wood, poor flora with very few species indicative of old woodland, and a name which itself suggests the wood's origins as a fox cover. There is a bridle path through the wood.

Burbage Wood, Hinckley

(Hinckley & Bosworth Borough) - SP 450941   O.S. Map No. 140

The wood is owned and managed by Hinckley & Bosworth Borough Council as part of a Country Park, and there is public access. It is described in detail in chapter thirteen.

Cloud Wood, Breedon-on-the-Hill

(North West Leicestershire District) - SK 417214   O.S. Map No. 129

This site is now owned and managed by the LRTNC. Access is restricted to members of the Trust, though there are public open days which are advertised in the local press. The site is described in detail in chapter thirteen.

Great Merrible Wood, Great Easton

(Harborough District). - SP 835963   O.S. Map No. 141
This wood is owned and managed by the LRTNC. It contains many giant coppice stools and the largest colony of herb paris in the county. Parts of the wood are ridge and furrow. There are two or three very old boundary pollards, and superb shows of bluebells in the spring.

Holly Hayes Wood, Coalville

(North West Leicestershire District) - SK 443154   O.S. Map No. 129
There are several footpaths through this wood, which appears to be a secondary woodland developed on former heathland. There is bilberry and hard fern within it, yet alongside a stream on one edge are carpets of wood anemones. An in-depth study of the site would be interesting.

Lady Wood, Stretton

(Rutland) - SK 963179   O.S. Map No. 130
A public footpath is present along one edge of this wood, which is on the Lincolnshire border. Several specimens of wild service-tree can be seen, as can the effects of deer damage. As a result of browsing there is an almost total lack of natural regeneration and a sparse shrub layer.

Martinshaw Wood, Ratby/Groby

(Hinckley & Bosworth Borough) - SK 510072   O.S. Map No. 140
Owned and managed by the Woodland Trust, this wood has easy public access. A large ancient woodland, it is a good example of a wood which has had nearly all of its semi-natural stands removed. It was subsequently re-planted with conifers.

Outwoods, Loughborough

(Charnwood Borough) - SK 514163   O.S. Map No. 129
This is another site badly affected by re-planting with conifers, though these are now being removed. Rhododendron invasion can also be seen, but again efforts are being made to eradicate the species. The site is owned and managed by Charnwood Borough Council, and there is easy public access.

Piper Wood, Long Whatton

(North West Leicestershire District) SK 477216   O.S. Map No. 129
This is a privately owned woodland, to which there is definitely no public access. However a public footpath runs along the western edge, and from this excellent views of the massive boundary earthworks can be obtained. Large colonies of wood melick occur on the earthworks. The southern part of the wood is suffering badly from sycamore invasion.

Prior's Coppice, Brooke/Leighfield

(Rutland) - SK 843052   O.S. Map No. 141
This wood is owned and managed by the LRTNC, and there is public access to the site. It is described in detail in chapter thirteen.

Swithland Wood, Newtown Linford/Swithland

(Charnwood District) - SK 537129   O.S. Map No. 129
Owned and managed by the Bradgate Park Trust, there is public access to this site. It is the most important woodland in Leicestershire and Rutland for nature conservation (see chapter 15), and there are many features of interest. It contains magnificent stands of both sessile and pedunculate oak, and also small-leaved lime. The latter is more frequent here than in any other wood in the county. The history and vegetation of the wood are described at length in Woodward (1993).

[Bluebells]

Willesley Wood, Ashby-de-la-Zouch

(North West Leicestershire District) SK 340150   O.S. Map No. 128
Situated in the National Forest, this is a large, newly planted site, in an attractive location. It is owned and managed by the Woodland Trust, and there is public access.

Appendix Two

National Vegetation Classification

The National Vegetation Classification (NVC) has been developed over many years and is now being adopted by ecologists in Britain as the standard vegetation classification system. It is highly complex, the woodland and scrub communities being described at length in Rodwell (1991). Whitbread and Kirby (1992) have, however produced a very useful simplified account.

    The community names are made up of a code letter and number, followed by the scientific names of one, two, or occasionally three of the characteristic plant species likely to be present. (The English names of the plants can be found in Appendix Three.)

    No detailed study using the NVC has yet been made of the woodland and scrub communities found in Leicestershire and Rutland, but from the information that is available the following community types appear to be present:

W1   *Salix cinerea — Galium palustre*   *(woodland)*

    Found as a fringe around the margins of reservoirs, gravel pits and the like, throughout the counties.

W5   *Alnus glutinosa — Carex paniculata*   *(woodland)*

    A rare type in Leicestershire, occurring only as very small patches of woodland, mainly on the coalfield in the north-west, and in Charnwood (for example Roecliffe Spinney).

W6   *Alnus glutinosa — Urtica dioica*   *(woodland)*

    An uncommon type, found mainly on flood plains.

W7   *Alnus glutinosa – Fraxinus excelsior – Lysimachia nemorum*
                                                      (woodland)

    Uncommon and largely confined to Charnwood Forest and the coalfield. Perhaps the best example is at Grace Dieu Wood.

W8   *Fraxinus excelsior — Acer campestre — Mercurialis perennis*
                                                      (woodland)

    Frequent outside the Charnwood and coalfield areas, it sometimes forms large species-rich woodlands, as at Prior's Coppice and Cloud Wood.

W10   Quercus robur — Pteridium aquilinum — Rubus fruticosus
(woodland)

Frequent in Charnwood Forest, the coalfield, and central Rutland areas. Rare elsewhere. Burley Wood and Swithland Woods contain fine examples.

W16   Quercus spp. — Deschampsia flexuosa   **(woodland)**

A rare type, confined to Charnwood and the coalfield, as at Southwood.

W21   Crataegus monogyna — Hedera helix   **(scrub)**

Widespread as scrub on neglected grassland, waste ground and hedges.

W22   Prunus spinosa — Rubus fruticosus   **(scrub)**

Widespread as scrub on neglected ground.

W23   Ulex europaeus — Rubus fruticosus   **(scrub)**

Local but sometimes forms dense stands, as at Luffenham Heath golf course.

W24   Rubus fruticosus — Holcus lanatus   **(underscrub)**

Widespread on waste ground, neglected grassland, gardens, etc.

W25   Pteridium aquilinum — Rubus fruticosus   **(underscrub)**

Locally frequent on the margins of woods, and sometimes forming glades within, mainly in Charnwood and the coalfield.

Appendix Three : *Names of Plants mentioned in the Text*

Common name (other local name) Scientific name

Alder	Alnus glutinosa
Alder Buckthorn	Frangula alnus
Ash	Fraxinus excelsior
Aspen	Populus tremula
Beech	Fagus syvatica
Betony	Stachys officinalis
Bilberry	Vaccinium myrtillus
Bird's-nest Orchid	Neottia nidus-avis
Blackthorn	Prunus spinosa
Bluebell	Hyacinthoides non-scripta
Bracken	Pteridium aquilinum
Bramble (Blackberry)	Rubus fruticosus agg.
Broad Buckler-fern	Dryopteris dilatata
Cleavers (Goosegrass)	Galium aparine
Common Cow-wheat	Melampyrum pratense
Common Marsh-bedstraw	Galium palustre
Common Nettle (Stinging Nettle)	Urtica dioica
Common Reed	Phragmites australis
Common Spotted-orchid	Dactylorhiza fuchsii
Cow Parsley	Anthriscus sylvestris
Cowslip	Primula veris
Crab Apple	Malus sylvestris
Creeping Soft-grass	Holcus mollis
Crested Cow-wheat	Melampyrum cristatum
Devil's-bit Scabious	Succisa pratensis
Dog's Mercury	Mercurialis perennis
Dogwood	Cornus sanguinea
Early-purple Orchid	Orchis mascula
Early Dog-violet	Viola reichenbaciana
Elder	Sambucus nigra
Elm	Ulmus sp.
English Elm	Ulmus procera
Field Maple	Acer campestre
Goldenrod	Solidago virgaurea
Goldilocks Buttercup	Ranunculus auricomus
Gorse	Ulex europaeus
Great Wood-rush	Luzula sylvatica
Greater Butterfly-orchid	Platanthera chlorantha
Greater Tussock-sedge	Carex paniculata
Grey Willow	Salix cinerea
Guelder-rose	Viburnum opulus
Hairy St. John's-wort	Hypericum hirsutum
Hairy Wood-rush	Luzula pilosa
Hard Fern	Blechnum spicant
Hard Shield-fern	Polystichum aculeatum
Hawthorn	Crataegus monogyna
Hazel	Corylus avellana
Heath Spotted-orchid	Dactylorhiza maculata ssp. ericetorum
Heather	Calluna vulgaris
Hemp-agrimony	Eupatorium cannabinum
Herb Paris	Paris quadrifolia
Holly	Ilex aquifolium
Honeysuckle	Lonicera periclymenum
Ivy	Hedera helix
Lesser Burdock	Arctium minus
Lily-of-the-valley	Convallaria majalis
Marsh-marigold (Kingcup)	Caltha palustris
Marsh Valerian	Valeriana dioica
Meadowsweet	Filipendula ulmaria
Moschatel	Adoxa moschatellina
Nettle-leaved Bellflower	Campanula trachelium
Oak	Quercus sp.
Opposite-leaved Golden-saxifrage	Chrisosplenium oppositifolium
Pale Sedge	Carex pallescens
Pedunculate Oak	Quercus robur
Pendulous Sedge	Carex pendula
Primrose	Primula vulgaris
Purple Small-reed	Calamagrostis canescens
Ragged-robin	Lychnis flos-cuculi
Ramsons (Wild Garlic)	Allium ursinum
Red Campion	Silene dioica
Remote Sedge	Carex remota
Rhododendron	Rhododendron ponticum
Rowan (Mountain Ash)	Sorbus aucuparia
Sanicle	Sanicula europaea
Sessile Oak (Durmast Oak)	Quercus petraea
Silver Birch	Betula pendula
Small-leaved Elm	Ulmus minor ssp. minor
Small-leaved Lime	Tilia cordata
Small Teasel	Dipsacus pilosus
Smooth-stalked Sedge	Carex laevegata
Soft-rush	Juncus effusus
Spreading Bellflower	Campanula patula
Sycamore	Acer pseudoplatanus
Thin-spiked Wood-sedge	Carex strigosa
Toothwort	Lathraea squamaria
Tufted Hair-grass	Deschampsia cespitosa
Water Avens	Geum rivale
Wavy Hair-grass	Deschampsia flexuosa
Wild Basil	Clinopodium vulgare
Wild Cherry	Prunus avium
Wild Service-tree	Sorbus torminalis
Willow	Salix sp.
Wood-sedge	Carex sylvatica
Wood Anemone	Anemone nemorosa
Wood Forget-me-not	Myosotis sylvatica
Wood Horsetail	Equisetum sylvaticum
Wood Melick	Melica uniflora
Wood Millet	Milium effusum
Wood Sage	Teucrium scorodonia
Wood Sorrel	Oxalis acetosella
Wood Speedwell	Veronica montana
Wood Vetch	Vicia sylvatica
Woodruff	Galium odoratum
Wych Elm	Ulmus glabra
Yellow Archangel	Lamiastrum galeobdolon
Yellow Pimpernel	Lysimachia nemorum
Yellow Star-of-Bethlehem	Gagea lutea
Yorkshire-fog	Holcus lonatus

References

For list of abbreviations see p. 150

Chapter 1
1. Farnham (1930) pp.100-107

Chapter 2
1. Roberts, N. and David, C. in Boucher (1994) p.52. Much research is now in hand on pollen analysis from these palaeochannels, and the next decade is expected to see a huge increase in environmental reconstruction, particularly as it concerns woodland.
2. Much of the outline given in this section, (including figure 2.4) and part of that in chapter 3, is based on discussions between the authors and Peter Liddle of Jewry Wall Museum, Leicester, and on the contents of both of his volumes of *'The Present State of Knowledge'* of Leicestershire Museums Service.
3. Liddle (1982) pp.42-43.

Chapter 3
1. Bourne, J., in Phythean-Adams (1978) pp.13-16. Figure 3.2 is based on the map on p.15.
2. Phythean-Adams (1978) Figure 3.3 is based on the map on p.12.
3. This section and figure 3.1 are based on data from Cox (1971).
4. Fox, H.F.S (1989)

Chapter 4
1. The two volumes of the Phillimore edition of Domesday Book, ed. J. Morris (1979, 1980) have been used as the basis of this section.
2. Rackham (1980), chapter 9.
3. Squires (1991) pp.40-42.

Chapter 5
1. Reproduced by permission of the Biblioteque Nationale, Paris.
2. Diagram – Paul Stamper in Astill and Grant (1988) p.131, used by permission.
3. Cantor (1970-71)
4. Squires,A.E. (1991)

Chapter 6
1. VCH Leics. vol. 3 p.41
2. Hoskins, (1963-64).
3. Much of the material for this paragraph comes from LMVN.

Chapter 7
1. Cal. Charter Rolls, 1226-1257 p.408.
2. LRO, Winstanley Papers MSS, DG5/480

3. The map is based on details in the Winstanley Papers , LRO DG/5; Hastings Collection, California; LMVN; LMVN(MSS); PRO DL papers; Hastings MSS vol I; Nichols vol IV; Cal. Pat. R. 1292-1301; Volumes of the Cal. IPM; TLAHS vol XI.
4. PRO, DL 43/14/6
5. PRO, DL 44/711
6. PRO, DL 44/679
7. PRO, DL 39/5/14
8. PRO, DL 44/711
9. Earl Cowper's records vol. I, p.286
10. PRO, DL 29/1/3
11. PRO, DL 29/278/11987
12. PRO, DL 39/5/14
13. Nichols 2/1/783
14. *Ibid.*
15. PRO, DL 43/14/6
16. Fox and Russell (1940) p.68
17. Nichols 2/1/784
18. Nichols 3/2/575
19. PRO, DL 43/4/6
20. *Ibid.*
21. Fox and Russell (1948) p.134
22. PRO, DL 44/711
23. Farnham Bequest, LRO, quoting Hastings MSS at Ashby.
24. Nichols 4/2/1001
25. PRO, DL 39/5/14
26. LMVN p.302
27. TLAHS, vol. XXIII, p.241
28. VCH (L) vol 2 p.265
29. Cal Charter R. 1226-57 p.193
30. Turner (1901) p.57
31. Hastings Collection, California.
32. *Ibid*
33. BL Add MSS 38444
34. LRO DE7/1/65/5
35. VCH (R) vol. 2, p.188
36. Cal. Close R. (1227-31) p. 265
37. Cal. Pat. R. (1281-92) p.455
38. VCH Rutland, vol. 1. p.257
39. Speed's map of Rutland, (1611)
40. Turner's *'Select Pleas'*, p.48
41. PRO C 143/1 folio 24
42. VCH (R) vol.2 p.13
43. Cal. Close R. (1226-27)
44. For a detailed history of the Charnwood Landscape see Squires,A.E., in Crocker J. (1981)
45. Hilton (1947) p.61
46. Milwood (1972) pp.218-234

47. The map is based on a number of sources, especially LMVN; Farnham 1912; Hastings Collection, California; LRO Grey MSS DG24; LRO Herrick MSS DG9 and others.
48. Pitt (1809) p.174
49. Potter (1842) p.157
50. The Act, awards and maps are in LRO
51. For a more detailed treatment of the Parks of Charnwood Forest see Squires and Humphreys (1986)
52. Squires and Humphrey (1986) footnote 1.
53. LRO DG/9 (1954-57)
54. Potter (1842) p.106
55. LMVN pp.112-113 and Ministers' Accounts (1512) LRO 5D33
56. Nichols vol. 3 p.1114
57. Squires and Humphrey (1986) p.131
58. PRO Misc. Chancery Inquisitions, 113-7
59. Loughborough Ministers' Accounts (1468-9)
60. Hastings Collection, California.
61. Phillimore (1912) vol. I p.250
62. LMVN pp.167-8

Chapter 8
1. Toulmin Smith (1964) pp.21-22
2. VCH (L) vol. 3 p.140
3. Valor Ecclesiasticus.
4. Dimmock Fletcher pp.237-240)
5. These remarks are based on the contents of Exchequer Papers in PRO, e.g. E314 and E323
6. The remarks in this paragraph are based mostly on Parker (1947)
7. BL Add. MSS 38444
8. *Ibid.*
9. PRO Depositions and Examinations Philip and Mary R2 and R2a
10. PRO E 315/462
11. PRO SP14/42
12. LRO 32'27/306
13. LRO Farnham Bequest D33/175
14. Shirley (1867) p.49
15. Hastings Collection, California
16. The authors are endebted to John Crocker for his help with the remarks on coalmining in this and subsequent sections.
17. LRO Survey of the manor of Bosworth (1594). DE 40/22/2-3
18. Nichols 3/2/739

Chapter 9
1. Figures from Bateman (1883)
2. Moscrop (1866) p.332
3. White (1846) p. 462
4. Curtis (1832) p.44
5. Grey Papers, Enville Hall
6. The remarks in this paragraph are based on Nichols 2/2/685-692
7. Shirley (1867) pp.141-147

8. Report of the commissioners of Woods, Forests and Lands of the Crown (1782-92)
9. Pitt (1809)
10. LRO Ferrers MSS 26 D53/2214
11. Pitt (1809) p.171
12. Woodward (1992) p.52
13. Figure 9.8 is from Ellis (1951)
14. VCH (L) vol.3 p.41

Chapter 10
1. James (1981) pp.208-209
2. *Ibid.* p.229
3. Report of the Committee on Hedgerows and Farm Timber (1955)
4. Census of Woodland (1965-67)
5. Strategy for the countryside (1971) p.20
6. *Ibid.* p.32
7. Wildlife Conservation in Charnwood Forest (1975)
8. Leicestershire Structure Plan: Written Statement (1976)
9. Wilkinson (1978) p.144
10. Census of Woodland Trees 1979-82, (1987)

Chapter 11
1. Horwood and Gainsborough (1933), p.xcvi-xcvii
2. Unpublished survey by M.B. Jeeves, LMS
3. M.B. Jeeves (1993)
4. See especially Peterken (1974) and Rackham (1980)
5. Flower illustrations from F.E. Hulme's Familiar Wild Flowers (1906)
6. Unpublished survey by M.B. Jeeves, LMS
7. Evans (1989)
8. Finch Papers, LRO DG67
9. Derek Lott of LMS kindly supplied the information on beetles.
10. The authors are indebted to John Crocker for this information
11. PRO DL 43/14/3 ff54-55

Chapter 12
1. Everett and Robinson (1990)
2. Peterken (1981)
3. Rodwell (1991)
4. Horwood and Gainsborough (1933)
5. Peterken (1981) p.153-154

Chapter 13
1. Morris (1979)
2. Map of the Manor of Breedon. (1758) LRO DG30/Ma/249/1-5
3. LMVN p.67
4. *Ibid.*
5. LRO DE 1982/81 p.6
6. Grey Papers at Enville Hall
7. LRO DE 311/890
8. Hastings Manuscripts vol I pp.34-35
9. Ibid. and Farnham Leics. Medieval Pedigrees.

10. LRO DE 1982/81 p.6
11. Grey Papers at Enville Hall
12. LRO DE 311/89
13. Map of Wilson (1758) LRO DG30/Ma/249/1-5
14. LMVN(MSS)
15. Thompson (1933) p.198
16. LRO DE 1982/91
17. Squires (1981) pp.32-36
18. Farnham (1912) p.104
19. Hastings Collection, California.
20. *Ibid.*
21. Squires and Humphreys (1986) p.74
22. *Ibid.*
23. *Ibid.* pp.74,76
24. *Ibid.* p.83
25. LMVN (MSS)
26. LMVN vol. 5 p.103
27. LRO DE 40/47
28. LMVN vol.5 p.107
29. *Ibid.*
30. *Ibid.*
31. Beds. RO. Wrest Papers L18/112
32. *Ibid.* L18/106
33. *Ibid.* L18/140
34. *Ibid.* L18/145
35. *Ibid.* L18/155
36. *Ibid.* L18/171
37. *Ibid.* L26/1073
38. *Ibid.* L26/1078
39. *Ibid.* L26/1121
40. Prior's map of Leicestershire (1777)
41. Throsby (1790) vol. 2 p.192
42. Beds R.O. Wrest Papers map of Burbage (1683) L26/1127
43. *Ibid.*
44. PRO SP14/194/4 Rentals and Surveys

45. *Ibid.*
46. Hastings Collection, California
47. *Ibid.*
48. Nichols 3/1/430b
49. *Ibid.*
50. PRO map MR33
51. Nichols 3/2/436b
52. Nichols 3/1/439
53. Nichols 3/1/463
54. LRO 35'29/478a
55. DRO. D2375M 168/8
56. Jeayes (1960) p.247
57. Cox (1971)
58. DRO D2735M 286/4/1
59. PRO E178 /1246
60. Hastings Collection, California
61. DRO D2375M 167/16
62. Plan of Southwood Common. Ticknall Estate Office.
63. LRO 5D33 No. 136
64. LMVN p.33
65 Hastings Collection, California.

Chapter 14

1. There is a fine photograph showing this in Primavesi and Evans (1988), plate 4.

Chapter 15

1. Kirby, K. in Usher (1986), pp.212-216
2. Goodfellow and Peterken (1981)
3. M.B. Jeeves (1993). Leicestershire Ancient Woodlands: their Flora, Vegetation and Nature Conservation Importance. Unpublished, but held by LMS

Chapter 16

1. Ratcliffe (1977)

Abbreviations used in the References and Bibiliography

BL	British Library. London
Cal. Close R.	Calendar of Close Rolls. Public Record Office
Cal. Charter R.	Calendar of Charter Rolls. Public Record Office
Cal. Pat. R.	Calendar of Patent Rolls. Public Record Office
DL	Duchy of Lancaster Papers. Public Record Office
DRO	Derbyshire Record Office
LMVN	G.F. Farnham. Leicestershire Medieval Village Notes (?-1933). Privately printed
LMVN(MS)	Manuscript version of the above, in LRO
Farnham Bequest	Manuscript papers of George F. Farnham. Leicestershire Record Office
Ferrers MSS	Manuscripts of the Ferrers Family. Leicestershire Record Office
Hastings Collection	Manuscripts of the Hastings family in Huntington Library, San Marino, California
LRO	Leicestershire Record Office.
LMS	Leicestershire Museums Service.
Nichols	John Nichols. The History and Antiquities of the county of Leicester. (1795-1811)
PRO	Public Record Office.
TLAHS	Transactions of the Leicestershire Archaeological and Historical Society.
VCH(L)	Victoria History of the County of Leicester (1907-64).
VCH(R)	Victoria History of the County of Rutland Vol. 1 (1908) and Vol. 2 (1935)

Bibliography

*T*he following are the works referenced in the preceding section, plus a selection of other works of relevance to woodlands in Leicestershire and Rutland.

Astill, Grenville and Grant, Annie. *The Countryside of Medieval England.* Basil Blackwell. (1988)

Bateman, John. *The Great Landowners of Great Britain and Ireland.* Harrison and Sons. fourth edition (1883)

Boucher, Keith (ed.) *Loughborough and its Region.* Loughborough University of Technology (1994)

Bourne, Jill. Some Anglo-Saxon Multiple Estates. in Phythian Adams, C. (1986)

Bunce, R.G.H. *A Field Key for Classifying British Woodland Vegetation.* part 1 (1982) and part 2 (1989). Institute for Terrestrial Ecology. Cambs.

Burton, William. *The Description of Leicestershire.* 2nd ed. W. Whittington, Lynn. (1717)

Cantor, L.M. The Medieval Parks of Leicestershire. *TLAHS* Vol. XLVI, pp. 9-24. (1970/71)

Cantor, L.M. The Medieval Hunting Grounds of Rutland. *Rutland Record,* No. 1, pp.13-18. (1980)

Cantor, L.M. (ed.). *The English Medieval Landscape.* Croom Helm, London. (1982)

Cantor L.M. *The Changing English Countryside.* Routledge and Kegan Paul. (1987)

Colebourne, Philip. *Ancient Woodland.* Hampshire County Council. (1983)

Colebourne, Philip and Gibbons, Robert. *Britain's Natural Heritage — Reading Our Countryside.* Blandford. (1987)

Cox, Barrie. *The Place Names of Leicestershire and Rutland.* unpublished Ph.D. thesis. Nottingham University. (1971)

Cox, J.C. *The Royal Forests of England.* Methuen and Co. London. (1905)

Crocker, J. The Habitat of Tetrilus macrophanthalmus (Kulczynski) in Leicestershire and Nottinghamshire *Bull. Brit. Arach. Soc.* 2(7) pp.117-123 (1973)

Crocker, J. (ed.) *Charnwood Forest, A Changing Landscape.* Sycamore Press, Wymondham, Melton Mowbray. (1981)

Dimmock Fletcher, W.G.D. Some Unpublished Documents Relating to Leicestershire Preserved in the Public Record Ofice. *TLAHS* Vol. XXIII pp. 18ff

Ellis, Colin D.B. *Leicestershire and the Quorn Hunt.* Edgar Backus, Leicester. (1951)

Evans, I. (ed.) *Burley Wood: Report on a Study of its History and Ecology.* Leicestershire Museums, Arts and Records Service, Leicester. (1989)

Everett, S. and Robinson, D.P. *Leicestershire Inventory of Ancient Woodland.* Nature Conservancy Council, Peterborough. (1990)

Farnham, G.F. *Quorndon Records.* Mitchell, Hughes and Clarke, London. (1912)

Farnham, G.F. *Leicestershire Medieval Pedigrees.* Leicester (1925)

Farnham, G.F. *Charnwood Forest and its Historians and the Charnwood Manors.* Edgar Backus, Leicester (1930)

Forestry Commission. *Census of Woodland 1947-49.* HMSO (1953)

Forestry Commission. *Census of Woodland 1965-67.* HMSO (1970)

Forestry Commission. *Report of the Committee on Hedgerows and Farm Timber.* HMSO (1955)

Fox, H.S.A. in Aston, M. Austin, D. and Dyer, C. (eds.) *English Medieval Settlement: Studies Dedicated to Maurice Beresford and J. Hurst.* (1989)

Fox, Levi and Russel, Percy. *Leicester Forest.* Edgar Backus, Leicester. (1948)

Godwin, Sir Harry. *History of the British Flora.* Cambridge University Press. (1975)

Goodfellow, S. and Peterken, G.F. A Method for Survey and Assessment of Woodlands for Nature Conservation Using Maps and Species Lists: The Example of Norfolk Woodlands. *Biological Conservation* Vol 21 pp.177-195 (1981)

Hartley, Robert. *The Medieval Earthworks of North-West Leicestershire, a Survey.* LMS. (1989)

Hartley, Robert F. *The Medieval Earthworks of Central Leicestershire.* LMS (1989)

Hilton, R.H. *The Economic Development of Some Leicestershire Estates in the Fourteenth and Fifteenth Centuries.* Oxford University Press, London. (1947)

Historical Manuscripts Commission. *Report on the Manuscripts of the Late Reginald Rawdon Hastings.* Vol 1. HMSO (1928)

Horwood, A.R. and Gainsborough, lord. *The Flora of Leicestershire and Rutland.* Oxford University Press, London. (1933)

Hoskins, W.G. *Leicestershire: An Illustrated Essay on the History of the Landscape.* Hodder and Stoughton, London (1957)

Hoskins, W.G. Provisional List of Deserted Medieval Villages in Leicestershire. *TLAHS* Vol. XXXIX, 1965-4, pp.24-33. (1963/64)

Humphrey, W. *Garendon Abbey.* University of Loughborough. (1982)

Jack, S. Monastic Lands of Leicestershire and their Administration on the Eve of the Dissolution. *TLAHS* Vol XLI pp. 9-40 (1965/66)

Jeayes, Isaac. *A Descriptive Catalogue of Derbyshire Charters.* (1960)

James, N. D. G. *A History of English Forestry.* Basil Blackwell, Oxford. (1981)

Jeeves, M.B. *Leicestershire Red Data Book: Vascular Plants.* Leicestershire and Rutland Trust for Nature Conservation, Leicester. (1993)

Jeeves, Michael, Bullock, John and Tobin, Robert (eds.) *A Guide to Nature Reserves in Leicestershire and Rutland.* Leicestershire and Rutland Trust For Nature Conservation, Leicester. (1994)

Kirby, M. *A Flora of Leicestershire.* Leicester. (1850)

Leicestershire County Council. *Strategy For The Countryside.* (1971)

Leicestershire County Council. *Leicestershire Structure Plan — Written Statement.* (1976, Reprinted July 1978)

Leicestershire County Council. *Replacement Structure Plan* (draft) (1993)

Leicestershire County Council *Nature Conservation Strategy* (draft) (1993)

Liddle, Peter. *The Present State of Knowledge. Vol 1 — To the end of the Roman Period.* Archaeological Report No. 4. LMS. 1982

Liddle, Peter. *The Present State of Knowledge. Vol 2 — Anglo-Saxon and Medieval Periods.* Archaeological Report No. 5. LMS. 1982

Mabey, Richard. *The Common Ground — A Place for Nature in Britain's Future?* Hutchinson. (1980)

Marren, Peter. *Britain's Ancient Woodland.* David and Charles, Newton Abbot. (1990)

McKinley, Richard. *An Edition of the Cartulary of Breedon Priory.* (unpublished MA thesis) University of Manchester. (1950)

Messenger, Guy. *The Flora of Rutland.* LMS (1971)

Millward, R. Saxon and Danish Leicestershire. in Pye, N. (ed.) *Leicester and its Region.* University of Leicester Press. London (1972)

Monk, John. *A General View of the Agriculture of the County of Leicester.* J Nichols, London. (1794)

Morris, John. (ed.) *Domesday Book : Leicestershire.* Phillimore, Chichester. (1979)

Morris, John. (ed.) *Domesday Book : Rutland. Phillimore,* Chichester. (1980)

Moscrop, W.J. A Report on the Farms of Leicestershire. *Journal of the Royal Agricultural Society of England,* 2nd series, Vol. 2, pp. 289-337. (1866)

Mott, F.T. et al. *The Flora of Leicestershire.* London. (1886)

Nature Conservancy Council. *Wildlife Conservation in Charnwood Forest.* Report by a Working Party. NCC Midlands Region. (1975)

Parker, L.A. *The Tudor Inclosure Movement In Leicestershire.* Unpublished Ph.D. thesis. London University. Copy in LRO.

Pennington, Winifred. *The History of British Vegetation.* English Universities Press. (1969)

Peterken, G.F. A Method for Assessing Woodland Flora for Conservation Using Indicator Species. *Biological Conservation.* Vol. 6 pp. 239-245. (1974)

Peterken, George. *Woodland Conservation and Management.* Chapman and Hall. (1981)

Peterken, G.F. and Welch R.C. (eds.) *Bedford Purlieus: Its History, Ecology and Management.* Monks Wood Experimental Station Symposium, No. 7 (1975)

Phillimore, W.P.W. (ed.) *Rotuli Hugonis de Welles.* Lincoln Record Society. (1912)

Phythian Adams, Charles. *Continuity and Fission: The Making of a Midland Parish.* Leicester University Press. (1978)

Phythian Adams, Charles. *The Norman Conquest of Leicestershire and Rutland.* Leicestershire Museums Service. (1986)

Pitt, William. *A General View of the Agriculture of the County of Leicester.* London. (1809)

Potter, T.R. *The History and Antiquities of Charnwood Forest.* London. (1842)

Primavesi, A.L. and Evans, P.A. *Flora of Leicestershire.* LMS (1988)

Prior, John. *Map of Leicestershire* (1777)

Rackham, Oliver. *Hayley Wood: Its History and Ecology.* Cambridge and Isle of Ely Naturalists' Trust, Cambridge (1975)

Rackham, Oliver. *Trees and Woods in the British Landscape.* Dent. (1976)

Rackham, Oliver. *Ancient Woodland: Its History, Vegetation and Uses in England.* Edward Arnold, London. (1980)

Rackham, Oliver. *The History of the Countryside.* Dent. (1980)

Rackham, Oliver. *The Woods of South-East Essex.* Rochford District Council. (1986)

Rackham, Oliver. *The Last Forest. The Story of Hatfield Forest.* Dent. (1989)

Ratcliffe, D.A. (ed.) *A Nature Conservation Review.* C.U.P Cambridge. (1977)

Report of the Commissioners of Woods, Forests and Lands of the Crown. (1787-92).
        Eleventh Report. London

Report on the Manuscript of the Late Reginald Rawden Hastings. Historical Manuscripts
        Commission. (1928)

Robinson, John Martin. *The English Country Estate.* Century/National Trust. (1988)

Rodwell, J.S. (ed.) *British Plant Communities, Volume 1. Woodland and Scrub.* CUP,
        Cambridge (1991)

Rose, F. and Harding, P.T. *Pasture Woodlands in Lowland Britain.* Institute for Terrestrial
        Ecology. Cambs. (1986)

Sher, M.B. *Wildlife Conservation Evaluation.* Chapman and Hall, London. (1986)

Shirley, E.P. *Some Account of English Deer Parks.* John Murray, London. (1867)

Speed, John. *Map of Rutland.* (1611)

Squires, A.E. The History of the Charnwood Landscape, in Crocker, J. (ed.) *Charnwood
        Forest: A Changing Landscape* (1981)

Squires, A.E. and Humphrey, W. *The Medieval Parks of Charnwood Forest.* Sycamore Press,
        Wymondham, Melton Mowbray. (1986)

Squires, Anthony. *Burbage Common and its History.* Bulletin of the Loughborough and
        District Archaeological Society. Vol III No. 2 Autumn 1991, pp.29-44. (1991)

Squires, Anthony. *Flitteris and Cold Overton: Two Medieval Deer Parks.* Rutland Record,
        No 12, pp. 47-52. (1992)

Stace, Clive. *New Flora of the British Isles.* CUP, Cambridge (1991)

Steele, R.C. and Welch, R.C. (eds.) *Monks Wood: A Nature Reserve Record.* Natural
        Environment Research Council, Huntingdon (1973)

Thompson, A. Hamilton. *Wyggeston Hospital Charters* (1933)

Throsby, John. *Select Views in Leicestershire.* Leicester (1789-90)

Toulmin Smith, L. (ed.) *The Itinerary of John Leland in or about the Years 1535-1543.* Centaur
        Press, London. (1964)

Turner, G.J. (ed.) *Select Pleas of the Forest.* Seldon Society, Vol. 13. London. (1901)

Usher, Michael B. *Wildlife Conservation Evaluation.* Chapman and Hall, London (1986)

Valor Ecclesiasticus. (1810-35). Record Commission, London

Watkins, Charles, *Woodland Management and Conservation.* David and Charles, Newton
        Abbot (1990)

Whitaker, J. *A Description of the Deer Parks and Paddocks of England.* Ballantyne, Hanson
        and Co. (1892)

Whitbread, A.M. and Kirby, K.J. *Summary of National Vegetation Classification Woodland
        Descriptions.* Joint Nature Conservation Committee, Peterborough. (1992)

White, William. *History, Gazeteer and Directory of Leicestershire and Rutland.* (1846)

Wilkinson, Gerald. *Epitaph for the Elm.* Hutchinson, London. (1978)

Woodward, Stephen. *Landscape of a Leicestershire Parish.* LMS. (1984)

Woodward, Stephen. *Swithland Wood, a Study of its History and Vegetation.* LMS. (1992)

Wright, J. *The History and Antiquities of the County of Rutland* (1684)

Index

*I*llustrations and the subjects of the maps and diagrams are shown in **bold**. Where a word is defined in the text, that page number is in *italics*. To aid identification, the woodlands are given their parish, and grid reference. Villages are given their administrative district, as a 'D' number, (see p.160 for a map and key to the disticts and OS grid).

Key to the Administrative Districts, and O.S. Grid

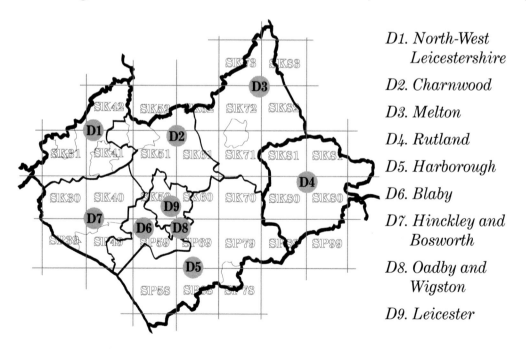

D1. North-West
    Leicestershire

D2. Charnwood

D3. Melton

D4. Rutland

D5. Harborough

D6. Blaby

D7. Hinckley and
    Bosworth

D8. Oadby and
    Wigston

D9. Leicester